the Wilds

Man ruined his life in sin

THERE4

God's remedy is Jesus Christ.

How can I show my thankfulness to God for such deliverance?

A Six-week Bible Study of Romans 12

By Rand Hummel

Other Titles by Rand Hummel
The Dark Side of the Internet
Fear Not
Five Smooth Stones
God & I Time Treasures Volume 1 & 2
God is... Learning About My God
James: A Guidebook to Spiritual Maturity
Jonah's Magnificent God
Joseph: A Man With Character
Lest You Fall
New Testament Postcards
1 Peter: Living in the Face of Ridicule
Philippians—The Secret of Outrageous, Contagious Joy!
Titus: Living a God-Centered Life in a Self-Centered World
Turn Away Wrath
What Does God Say About My Sin?

All Scripture is quoted from the Authorized King James Version.

There4...(Romans 12)
A Six-week Bible Study
By Rand Hummel
Cover design by Craig Stouffer

PO Box 509
Taylors, SC 29687-0009
Phone: (864) 268-4760
Fax: (864) 292-0743

ISBN: 978-0982942437

Table of Contents

Section 3: Therefore, how can I show my thankfulness to God for such deliverance?

Therefore...

I beseech you therefore, brethren, by the mercies of God, that you present your bodies a living sacrifice, holy, acceptable unto God, which is your reasonable service. (Romans 12:1)

Dear Bible Study Friend,

How many things does a person need to know in order to live and die a happy, contented, fulfilled life? According to the second question of the Heidelberg Catechism of 1563, he needs to know only three: one, how great are my miseries and sin; two, how I can be delivered from my misery and sin; and three, how I am to be thankful to God for such deliverance.

When Paul wrote the word "therefore," he was not just giving a general glimpse of the 315 verses of Romans 1-11, but he was specifically explaining man's complete ruin in sin (Romans 1-3) and God's perfect remedy in Christ (Romans 4-11). Knowing what we were and what we are because of what God has done should impact the way we live each day.

Strong Bible teaching should always be accompanied by solid Bible application. Doctrine without application could give us big heads and little hearts. Application without doctrine could result in full hearts and empty heads.

It is not difficult to understand the extreme wickedness of our own hearts, but it is difficult to clearly explain what God has done for us and why He would treat such wicked sinners with such love. The conclusion of Romans 11 reveals to us how untraceable and unsearchable God's deliverance, mercy, and grace to us really is.

Enjoy your study of Romans 12. Together we will learn the many ways we can say "Thank You!" to a God who has done so much for us!

Rand

Rand Hummel

Section 1

Man has ruined his life in sin.

(Romans 1-3)

God's remedy is in Jesus Christ.

(Romans 4-11)

Therefore, how can I show my thankfulness to God for such deliverance?

(Romans 12)

Therefore

Monday: Romans 1

Man has completely ruined his life in sin.

"Lord, do I truly understand the depth of depravity and the extreme wickedness of my own heart?"

Paul starts out his letter with a dark, dark picture of man's heart. Man has completely ruined his life in sin. Man is innately wicked with a bent towards evil. The following four verses from Romans 1 give a general direction of what man is really made of. This is not (and never will be aside from God's deliverance) a pretty picture. Meditate on Romans 1:18, 21, 25, and 32 and thank God for His deliverance from such a life.

Romans 1:18 **For the wrath of God is revealed from heaven against all ungodliness and unrighteousness of men, who hold the truth in unrighteousness** (suppress or hold the truth down by their wickedness). Did it ever occur to you that God gets angry? Why? What is so important to God that would actually cause Him to unleash His wrath? List the two recipients of God's wrath in Romans 1:18 and, to the best of your ability, try to define or describe each of them.

un-________________: ____

____

un-________________: ____

____

When men give their sin (unrighteousness, wickedness) free reign, they are choosing to push God, and the truth about God, totally out of their hearts, minds, and lives. They know better! (And so do we.) Ignoring what God has said is like holding an inflated balloon under water; the truth cannot be hidden for very long before it pops back up and reveals how wicked we really are. By the way, the reason that God hates sin so much is that He loves us so much. Sin is the great separator. Those who reject God's loving forgiveness will be separated from Him for eternity. Quickly explain when you trusted Christ's death on the cross for the payment of your sin. ________________________________

____

____

____

____

____

Romans 1:20b-21 **...so that they are without excuse: because that, when they knew God, they glorified Him not as God, neither were thankful; but became vain in their imaginations, and their foolish heart was darkened.** What six words at the end of Romans 1:20 nail those who like to blame others for their trouble and sin? ____________________

____

____

These guys knew better, but chose to ignore and look down upon God. The opposite of "glorifying God" is actually "blaspheming God." Their incredible love for sin created an overwhelming hatred for God. Read Matthew 6:24 and explain how it relates to the empty, dark thinkers of Romans 1:21. ____

____

____

____

These guys started thinking up foolish ideas of what God was like to justify their own sin. A loving, forgiving, holy God was not good enough for them because such a God would hold them responsible for their sin. So they had to make up their own pretend gods. It is pretty foolish (even stupid) to make God in your own image. If you really were bent on stealing, cheating, and lying, what kind of pretend god would you make up in your mind? ___________

____

____

____

____

Romans 1:25 **Who changed the truth of God into a lie, and worshipped and served the creature more than the Creator, who is blessed for ever. Amen.** Idolatry is an ancient form of self-worship. Men made up pretend gods that would allow them to do whatever they wanted to do. They were self-serving gods. They twisted God's Word to say what they wanted it to say which gave them permission to worship and serve themselves. Sound familiar? List the names of two media or sports superstars (who seem to be worshipping themselves instead of God) and explain why you chose them and how you think their lifestyles displease God. __________

____

____

____

Romans 1:32 **Who knowing the judgment of God, that they which commit such things are worthy of death, not only do the same, but have pleasure in them that do them.** At whatever point our wicked, depraved hearts ignore or even mock an all-knowing, ever-present God, we are in trouble. Can you imagine defending yourself before a judge who was there when you committed the crime, and not only knows what you did, but why (the entire thought process) you did it! We can choose our sin but not its consequences. According to Romans 6:23, what is the ultimate consequence (wage or payment) of sin? ___________________________

As a sinner, I deserve to die! And so do you. Some not only choose to sin themselves, but find **pleasure in** others who sin—giving their hearty approval by paying to be entertained by it. The excuse, "I'm not the one doing it!" while watching the sinful acts on-screen or online won't cut it before God. Describe how finding pleasure in others who live in sin has become the basis for most entertainment plots in popular movies and current TV today. ____________________

____

____

What do you do to protect yourself from such entertainment? ____________________

____

____

____

Those who ignore God's Word and push it out of their lives,
will soon ignore God and push Him out of their lives.
They will worship themselves as their own gods
and will receive what they ask for
—a life "without" God—
without God forever and forever.

Tuesday: Romans 1

When man gives up on God, does God ever give up on him?

"Lord, does there come a point when You give up on men and let them receive the consequences of their sin?"

As Paul paints a very dark picture of man in Romans 1, there are three phrases (the first one repeated) that should cause unbelievers to shudder and tremble. Even though this is not what God desires, He inspired these words of hopelessness and helplessness. Remember, God is **not willing that any should perish** (2 Peter 3:9). The ultimate of God's wrath is not found in chastisement or correction, it is sadly observed when God gets quiet.

Wherefore, God also gave them up...(v. 24)
For this cause, God gave them up...(v. 26)
God gave them over...(v. 28)

Romans 1:18 **For the wrath of God is revealed from heaven against all ungodliness and unrighteousness of men, who hold the truth in unrighteousness.** We cannot compare the **wrath of God** with the wrath of men. Our anger is often selfish, out-of-control, emotional, and foolish. God's wrath is motivated by and wrapped up in love. It is because of His extreme love for us, His infinite knowledge of how sin can impact our relationship with others, our relationship with Him, and our eternity, that His wrath is **revealed against all ungodliness and unrighteousness.** When men refuse to listen and repeatedly tell God to leave them alone, there comes a time when God does what they ask for and stops convicting them. When God gets angry, He does not yell and scream, He gets quiet. Why do you think it is very dangerous for God to stop convicting a man? ____

____

____

____

Romans 1:24a **Wherefore God also gave them up to uncleanness through the lusts of their own hearts**. Because these Romans 1 men and women chose to love their sin and ignore God, God **gave them up!** Another way of saying this is that God "gave them over to" what they craved and desired. They did not want God! They did want sin. God simply gave them what they wanted, desired, and lusted after—uncleanness! When men allow their fleshly desires to become their gods (and the true God steps back and allows them to have what they want), they are reducing themselves to the point of acting like nothing more than an animal. This is sad.

You know the great feeling that a good, hot shower gives after a tiring day at school or work, after an intense game of soccer, basketball, or volleyball, or after a long trip to THE WILDS Christian Camp in a school bus without air conditioning? There is something incredibly refreshing about being clean after such activities. Too bad we don't look at our inward cleanliness in the same way. Physically we don't like to be dirty; can you say the same thing about your spiritual life? Immoral sin will make you feel dirty; God's forgiveness will make you completely clean. Read Psalm 19:12-14, Psalm 32:5-6, Psalm 51:9-10, and 1 John 1:9; pick your favorite of these verses and write a thank-you note to God for what He promises in the passage you chose. ____

____

____

____

____

Romans 1:26a **For this cause God gave them up unto vile affections.** To those who purposely chose to believe a lie about God (believing that He is not our sovereign Ruler who can make demands on our lives) and chose to worship the things that God created instead of the Creator God Himself, God again **gave them over to** their degrading, shameful, immoral desires. They reduced their behavior to include sexual behavior that would not be natural for a squirrel, a bird, or even a hog. The word "perversion" could be used to describe their sinful behavior as they twisted and distorted God's words to do what they wanted to do in the first place. Is there anything in your life that you know is not best, but you justify or excuse it to keep it in your life? If so, from what we just learned, what should you do? ______________________________

____

____

Romans 1:28 **And even as they did not like to retain God in their knowledge, God gave them over to a reprobate mind, to do those things which are not convenient.** Too many today live according to their "likes" and "dislikes." Broccoli: If they don't "like" it, they don't eat it. Exercise: If they don't "like" it, they don't do it! Parents' rules: If they don't "like" them, they don't obey them. God's Word: If they don't "like" what it says, they ignore it and do what they want to do. The darkened hearts of the Romans 1 followers **did not like to retain God in their knowledge.** They ignored God and refused to acknowledge His presence, His power, or His preeminence over their lives. (Hopefully you do not fall into this same mind-set.) Because of this, God *gave them over to* their empty, foolish thinking. They started doing what they were thinking! And what they did should have never been done. Think sin, then multiply it by ten, and you might get close to the depravity their foolish thinking led them to.

Even as believers, we have to guard our thought lives or we too will end up foolishly doing the foolish things that we foolishly think about. The word **reprobate** has the concept of being unworthy, unacceptable, unapproved, or undiscerning. On a daily basis, does God accept or approve of your thoughts? Explain why, why not, and what needs to change in your heart and mind. ____

____

____

____

____

So, when man gives up on God, does God ever give up on him? God is not willing that any should perish, but neither will He populate heaven with well-programmed robots or empty-headed puppets. When a man tells God, "Leave me alone!" God may just give that man what he wants, and leave him alone—forever and ever.

Wednesday: Romans 1

What is the extent of man's depravity? Are we capable of any and all sins?

"Lord, please protect me from this long list of sins that seems to describe those who have foolishly chosen to reject You and worship themselves."

When Paul said, **God gave them over to a reprobate mind, to do those things which are not convenient**, he was simply saying that God gave them over to their depraved thinking which resulted in a long list of inexcusable and sinful behaviors. Sad to say, most of the sins on the Romans 1 list are commonplace in our entertainment world, cyber world, and real world today. (Hopefully though, not in your life.)

There are actually two lists in Romans 1:29-32. The first is centered on the words **being filled with** and **full of**, and refers to the attitudes or thoughts of the heart. The second list starts with the last word of verse 29, **whisperers**, continues through verse 32, and describes the actions of these Romans 1 God-haters. What did Jesus teach in Matthew 12:34-35 and again in Matthew 15:18-19 that mirrors what Paul is teaching here? ____________________

____

____

Solomon also knew that although we are not what we think we are, we are what we think. How does Proverbs 23:7 support both the teaching of Paul in Romans and Christ in Matthew? ______

____

____

In our study (both today and tomorrow) we will meditate on these lists, be warned of the extent of man's depravity, and consider the consequence of each thought or action. Today we will deal with the "Attitudes" or "As he thinketh in his heart" list. Tomorrow we will look at the "Actions" or the "So is he" list. After each word, list of synonyms, and related Scripture, explain how these sinful attitudes or thoughts could impact our relationships with both God and others.

"As he thinketh in his heart"

1. How could **unrighteousness** impact my relationship with God and others? ____________________

____

____

unrighteousness (what ought not to be; unjust; wrong and not right; uncomfortable with what is right and good): **But unto them that are contentious, and do not obey the truth, but obey unrighteousness, indignation and wrath, tribulation and anguish, upon every soul of man that doeth evil, of the Jew first, and also of the Gentile.** Romans 2:8-9

2. How could **fornication** impact my relationship with God and others? ____________________

____

____

fornication (to commit any sexual sin, lewdness, immoral, perverted, morally unclean): **But fornication, and all uncleanness, or covetousness, let it not be once named among you, as becometh saints.** Ephesians 5:3

3. How could **wickedness** impact my relationship with God and others? ____________________

____

____

wickedness (evil in nature, innately bad, utter depravity): **And the Lord said unto him, Now do ye Pharisees make clean the outside of the cup and the platter; but your inward part is full of ravening and wickedness.** Luke 11:39

4. How could **covetousness** impact my relationship with God and others? ________________

____

____

covetousness (greediness, the desire for more motivated by a discontented heart, the longing to have more and more of what God never intended us to have): **And He said unto them, Take heed, and beware of covetousness: for a man's life consisteth not in the abundance of the things which he possesseth.** Luke 12:15

5. How could **maliciousness** impact my relationship with God and others? ________________

____

____

maliciousness (evil, bad, a habitual wickedness rooted in the mind, evil from the inside out): **Wherefore laying aside all malice, and all guile, and hypocrisies, and envies, and all evil speakings, as newborn babes, desire the sincere milk of the word, that ye may grow thereby.** 1 Peter 2:1-2

6. How could **envy** impact my relationship with God and others? ________________

____

____

envy (jealousy, bothered to the point of thinking evil at the success and happiness of others, wanting what others have and not wanting them to have it): **For we ourselves also were sometimes foolish, disobedient, deceived, serving divers lusts and pleasures, living in malice and envy, hateful, and hating one another.** Titus 3:3

7. How could **murder** impact my relationship with God and others? ________________

____

____

murder (slaughter; taking the life of someone for hateful, vengeful, or envious purposes; no respect for human life): **For from within, out of the heart of men, proceed evil thoughts, adulteries, fornications, murders.** Mark 7:21

8. How could **debating** impact my relationship with God and others? ________________

____

____

debate (contentious, argumentative, quarrelsome, a lover of strife): **For ye are yet carnal: for whereas there is among you envying, and strife, and divisions, are ye not carnal, and walk as men?** 1 Corinthians 3:3

9. How could **deceit** impact my relationship with God and others? ________________

____

____

deceit (to bait, trick, or deceive): **For he that will love life, and see good days, let him refrain his tongue from evil, and his lips that they speak no guile.** 1 Peter 3 :10

10. How could **malignity** impact my relationship with God and others? ________________

____

____

malignity (evil-mindedness, thinking the worst of others, wicked disposition): **...God gave them up unto vile affections.** Romans 1:26a

Search me, O God, and know my heart: try me, and know my thoughts: and see if there be any wicked way in me, and lead me in the way everlasting.
Psalm 139:23-24

Thursday: Romans 1

A man's thoughts are an index to his character. What we think today we become tomorrow.

"Lord, please protect me from my own selfish thinking.
I do not want to become a Romans 1 statistic."

The attitudes we studied yesterday often result in the actions we will look at today. The depravity of our own hearts should cause us to shudder, fearing even the potential of our own wickedness. We must thank God for His daily provision of grace and mercy which keeps us from such depraved behavior. Romans 1:29-32 lists thirteen types of people who have given in to their depravity. By God's grace, may we never be accused of such actions or attitudes.

As a man thinks, so is he!

1. Could anyone accuse me of being a **whisperer**? If so, why? ______________________________

____

____

whisperers (a backbiting, malicious, secret slanderer; a lying gossip): **Where no wood is, there the fire goeth out: so where there is no talebearer, the strife ceaseth.** Proverbs 26:20

2. Could anyone accuse me of being a **backbiter**? If so, why? ______________________________

____

____

backbiters (a critical, insulting accuser): **Wherein they think it strange that ye run not with them to the same excess of riot, speaking evil of you: who shall give account to him that is ready to judge the quick and the dead.** 1 Peter 4:4-5

3. Could anyone accuse me of being a **hater of God**? If so, why? ______________________________

____

____

haters of God (to hate or abhor, therefore to turn away from or keep a distance from): **Can any hide himself in secret places that I shall not see him? saith the Lord. Do not I fill heaven and earth? saith the Lord.** Jeremiah 23:24

4. Could anyone accuse me of being **spiteful**? If so, why? ______________________________

____

____

despiteful (violent, arrogant insolence which attacks and persecutes others): **But chiefly them that walk after the flesh in the lust of uncleanness, and despise government. Presumptuous are they, selfwilled, they are not afraid to speak evil of dignities.** 2 Peter 2:10

5. Could anyone accuse me of being **proud**? If so, why? ______________________________

____

____

proud (ostentatiously proud, trying to look better than everyone around them): **For men shall be lovers of their own selves, covetous, boasters, proud, blasphemers, disobedient to parents, unthankful, unholy.** 2 Timothy 3:2

6. Could anyone accuse me of being **boastful**? If so, why? ______________________________

____

boasters (an empty pretender bragging about that which he does not possess or feats that he cannot accomplish): **For our gospel came not unto you in word only, but also in power, and in the Holy Ghost, and in much assurance; as ye know what manner of men we were among you for your sake.** 1 Thessalonians 1:5

7. Could anyone accuse me of being an **inventor of evil things**? If so, why?

___

inventors of evil things (always looking and searching for ways to be involved in moral wickedness): **Let love be without dissimulation. Abhor that which is evil; cleave to that which is good.** Romans 12:9

8. Could anyone accuse me of being **disobedient to parents**? If so, why?___

___

___

disobedient to parents (defiant, rebellious heart that treats a mom or a dad as if they were worthless): **A wise son maketh a glad father: but a foolish man despiseth his mother.** Proverbs 15:20

9. Could anyone accuse me of being **without understanding**? If so, why? ___

___

___

without understanding (undiscerning, no reasoning ability): **A prudent man foreseeth the evil, and hideth himself: but the simple pass on, and are punished.** Proverbs 22:3

10. Could anyone accuse me of being a **covenant breaker**? If so, why? ___

___

___

covenant breakers (untrustworthy, undependable, cannot trust what they say, promise breakers): **When thou vowest a vow unto God, defer not to pay it; for He hath no pleasure in fools: pay that which thou hast vowed.** Ecclesiastes 5:4

11. Could anyone accuse me of being **without natural affection**? If so, why?___

___

___

without natural affection (unloving, hateful, without normal family love which results in tension, divorce, abortion, abuse, rejection, etc.): **This is my commandment, That ye love one another, as I have loved you. Greater love hath no man than this, that a man lay down his life for his friends.** John 15:12-13

12. Could anyone accuse me of being **implacable**? If so, why? ___

___

___

implacable (unforgiving, quarrelsome, absolutely irreconcilable, refusing to talk, reason, or forgive): **If it be possible, as much as lieth in you, live peaceably with all men. Dearly beloved, avenge not yourselves, but rather give place unto wrath: for it is written, Vengeance is Mine; I will repay, saith the Lord.** Romans 12:18-19

13. Could anyone accuse me of being **unmerciful**? If so, why? ___

___

___

unmerciful (no compassion, without mercy, simply does not care about anyone other than themselves): **But whoso hath this world's good, and seeth his brother have need, and shutteth up his bowels of compassion from him, how dwelleth the love of God in him?** 1 John 3:17

"Lord, please protect me from this long list of sins that seems to describe those who have foolishly chosen to reject You and worship themselves. Please protect me from my own selfish thinking. I do not want to become a Romans 1 statistic."

Friday: Romans 2

Both the self-centered immoral person and the self-righteous moral person are inexcusable before God!

"Lord, please keep me from the evils and the pitfalls of both self-centeredness and self-righteousness."

Question: Are the good, moral people who reject God any better off than the wicked, immoral people who reject God?

Answer 1: No. Both actually "do" what they know is sin in others. (2:1-3)

Slowly read Romans 2:1-3. If someone offends you by being harsh, unkind, and hurtful, and you attack them with a mean, unloving, critical spirit, are you any better than they are? If you go on Facebook and start a hate-dialog against someone who has secretly slandered you, are you any better than they are? If you refuse to forgive someone from your past, or won't even consider meeting with them to reconcile your differences, are you any better than they are? Even an outwardly moral person can be a Romans 1:29-32 **implacable whisperer** or **backbiter**. Can you think of any attitudes in your own heart that could result in the actions that you hate in others? ____________________

____

____

____

Answer 2: No. Both look down on God's kindness, forbearance, and patience. (2:4)

Carefully read Romans 2:4. Too often we presume on the goodness of God. He is abundantly kind, incredibly tolerant, and inconceivably patient with each one of us! Too often we take this for granted. What if God gave us the same amount of kindness we give to others? What if God had the same level of tolerance toward our selfishness that we had toward those we live with? What if God lost His patience with us as often as we lose our patience with others? We would be in trouble. Using a dictionary or thesaurus, write out three or four synonyms for the following words.

- goodness: ____________________
- forbearance: ____________________
- longsuffering: ____________________

Answer 3: No. Both have hard, unbelieving hearts. (2:5)

Read Romans 2:5. This is a heart issue. The word **treasurest** means to store up in a safe place, and in this case, it is not gold (or even anything good) but the **wrath of God** that is being stored. God is patient! He is also just. Regardless of how religious a person is, if he chooses to reject Jesus Christ as Savior because of a stubborn (**hard**), unbelieving (**impenitent**) heart, he will someday experience the ultimate wrath of God unleashed. When you have time, read Revelation 16 and create a mental picture of God's wrath as revealed in the bowls of wrath. Why would anyone desire such wrath? ____________________

____

Answer 4: No. Both are "hearers" but not "doers" of God's Word. (2:6-13)

A slow read of Romans 2:6-13 reveals how important this truth is to God. He states His concern in verses 6-8 and then repeats it in verses 9-11. God is reminding us that He does not pick favorites, but blesses those who humbly obey, and judges those who stubbornly disobey. Pretty simple to understand. What does God promise to those who do evil? _____

____

What does God promise to those who do good? ______________________________

____

We choose whether we will receive **glory, honor**, and **peace** or **wrath, indignation, tribulation,** and **anguish**. What is your choice? ___________________________

____

____

Answer 5: No. Both forget that they cannot keep secrets from God. (2:16)

There is a day coming when **God will judge the secrets of men by Christ Jesus.** Some are good at keeping a secret from others and others tell the first person they meet. No one can keep a secret from an all-knowing, all-wise, omniscient God! God not only knows "what" you've done, He knows the motivation of your heart and "why" you did it. Some secrets are good! True servants serve God secretly and no one knows but God. Some secrets are bad. Sinners who think they have sinned secretly will someday see that with God, there are no secrets. What secret do you and God share that no one else on earth knows about? _______________

____

____

Answer 6: No. Both cause others to look down on God because of their wickedness. (2:24)

When professing believers live in sin, unbelievers laugh. They laugh at both the sinner and the Savior. To **blaspheme** is to discredit with impious, irreverent words, or as we would say today, to make God look weak, stupid, and irrelevant. The opposite of blaspheming God is **glorifying God** (1 Corinthians 10:31). Obedient, pure, godly lives glorify God as others see God empowering them to live holy, righteous lives in a wicked, God-hating world. So, as your friends watch your life, do they glorify or blaspheme God? ___________________________

Answer 7: No. Both forget that a real relationship with God is a "heart" issue—not based on what they do, but what they are. (2:28-29)

Read Romans 2:28-29. **Outwardly** we can conform and perform in such a way that we look good. Paul is reminding us that a true believer is **one inwardly**, whose **heart** has been changed by God's Spirit, who by trusting Christ is willing to be identified with Christ, to live for Christ, and to depend on Christ and Christ alone for eternal life. It is not what we have done for Christ, but what Christ has done for us. What are you trusting in? Your goodness or God's grace? Your morality or God's mercy? ____

Answer 8: No. **Therefore, thou art inexcusable, O man...and thinkest thou this, O man...that thou shalt escape the judgment of God?** (2:1-3)

Saturday: Romans 3

Man ruined his life in sin: for all have sinned. Jesus Christ is God's remedy: Who died for all.

"Lord, thank You for Your forgiveness!"

Romans 3 is one of the most convicting and comforting chapters of God's written Word. The first part of the chapter reminds me that I am a sinner. The final part reassures me that my sins have been forgiven by faith in Christ. It is good for me to be reminded of my sinful heart so that my expression of thanksgiving to God for His forgiveness may become a daily occurrence. Paul must have been thinking of Psalm 14 and 53 as God inspired him to write this nine-verse description of a depraved man's heart. In ninety-nine words, Paul describes the present heart of an unbeliever (which we must remember is the former heart of a believer). If you trusted Christ as a small child, this describes what you would have become without Christ. After each phrase below, write a prayer of thanksgiving that specifically thanks God for His mercy and grace that saved you from such depravity.

There is none righteous, no, not one: ______________________________

____

There is none who understands: ______________________________

____

There is none who seeks after God: ______________________________

____

They have all turned aside: ______________________________

____

They have together become unprofitable: ______________________________

____

There is none who does good, no, not one: ______________________________

____

Their throat is an open tomb (sepulchre): ______________________________

____

With their tongues they have practiced deceit: ______________________________

____

The poison of asps is under their lips: ______________________________

____

Whose mouth is full of cursing and bitterness: ______________________________

____

Their feet are swift to shed blood: ______________________________

____

Destruction and misery are in their ways: ______________________________

____

And the way of peace they have not known: ______________________________

____

There is no fear of God before their eyes: ______________________________

____

Romans 3:21 starts with the words "**But now**" which Paul uses to transition from what was to what is; from what we were destined to be to what we have been made to be; from what we could have accomplished in the flesh to what God has accomplished by His grace. Let us never forget what God has done and continues to do on a daily basis. He forgives, justifies, redeems (the list could go on and on). After each Bible phrase and explanation below, write a prayer of thanksgiving to God.

But now the righteousness of God without the law is manifested, being witnessed by the law and the prophets: (God has shown us a way to be right with Him without fulfilling the requirements of the law as Moses and the prophets promised.) ______________________

____

____

Even the righteousness of God which is by faith of Jesus Christ unto all and upon all them that believe: for there is no difference: (No matter who we are or what we have done, we are made right with God by placing our faith in Jesus Christ.) __________________________

____

____

For all have sinned, and come short of the glory of God: (All of us have sinned and fall way short of God's glorious perfection.) ______________________________________

____

____

Being justified freely by His grace through the redemption that is in Christ Jesus: (Unreservedly, through Jesus Christ, we have been freed from the penalty of our sin.) ________

____

____

Whom God hath set forth to be a propitiation through faith in His blood: (God sent Jesus to be sacrificed for my sin; He shed His blood for me.) ______________________________

____

____

To declare His righteousness for the remission of sins that are past, through the forbearance of God: (God knew that Jesus would pay for sin and was just in holding off His punishment for those who sinned in the past.)______________________________

____

____

To declare, I say, at this time His righteousness: (God is fair, just, and righteous in the way that He deals with both sinners and their sin.) ______________________________

____

____

That He might be just, and the justifier of him which believeth in Jesus: (God is always fair, especially in the way that He declares us sinners right in His sight as we put our faith and trust in Jesus Christ and Christ alone.) ______________________________

____

We have so very, very much to be thankful for. Can you imagine what it would be like for all eternity if God gave us what we deserved?

"Lord, thank You for Your forgiveness!"

Sunday Review and Meditation

"Lord, O how great is my wickedness, misery, and sin.
Thank You for Your forgiveness!"

Man has completely ruined his life in sin.

Read Monday's study and write one paragraph explaining what God taught you about yourself and Him.

When man gives up on God, does God ever give up on him?

Read Tuesday's study and write one paragraph explaining what God taught you about yourself and Him.

What is the extent of man's depravity? Are we capable of any and all sins?

Read Wednesday's study and write one paragraph explaining what God taught you about yourself and Him.

A man's thoughts are an index to his character. What we think today we become tomorrow.

Read Thursday's study and write one paragraph explaining what God taught you about yourself and Him.

Both the self-centered immoral person and the self-righteous moral person are inexcusable before God!

Read Friday's study and write one paragraph explaining what God taught you about yourself and Him.

Man ruined his life in sin: for all have sinned. Jesus Christ is God's remedy: Who died for all.

Read Saturday's study and write one paragraph explaining what God taught you about yourself and Him.

Section 2

Man has ruined his life in sin.
(Romans 1-3)

God's remedy is in Jesus Christ.

(Romans 4-11)

Therefore, how can I show my thankfulness to God for such deliverance?
(Romans 12)

Therefore

We learned in our first week's study how depraved and wicked a man's heart can become when he refuses to listen to God and pushes Him out of his life. Just as darkness is defined by the absence of light and cold is defined by the absence of heat, some say that evil could be defined as the absence of God. When God is rejected and despised, evil reigns. The answer to such a wicked, depraved, sinful heart is the rescue, redemption, and reconciliation through Jesus Christ. Romans 1-3 reminds us that man has ruined his life in sin; Romans 4-11 explains that God's remedy is in the death, burial, and resurrection of Jesus Christ. We are justified and sanctified in Christ and Christ alone.

Below is a brief outline of Romans 4-11 compiled by the outline guru Warren Wiersbe who is famous for his BE SERIES[1] commentaries. We will attempt to get a solid overview of these eight chapters in the next six days. What God has done for us wicked sinners is simply amazing. We should be so thankful.

Salvation (3:21-5:21—Righteousness Imputed)
- A. Justification explained (3:21-31)
- B. Justification expressed: the example of Abraham (4)
- C. Justification experienced (5)

Sanctification (6-8—Righteousness Imparted)
- A. Our new position in Christ (6)
- B. Our new problem in the flesh (7)
- C. Our new power in the Spirit (8)

Sovereignty (9-11—Righteousness Rejected)
- A. Israel's past election (9)
- B. Israel's present rejection (10)
- C. Israel's future redemption (11)

Monday: Romans 4

Justification Examined

jus·ti·fy, v. jus·ti·fied, jus·ti·fy·ing, jus·ti·fies

1. To demonstrate or prove to be just, right, or valid.
2. To declare free of blame; absolve.
3. To free (a human) of the guilt and penalty attached to grievous sin. Used of God.
4. In Christian theology, justification is God's act of reckoning a sinner righteous before God by the imputation of Christ's righteousness.

As a sinner, I need forgiveness. Forgiveness is a promise (not a feeling) that my sin has been covered, dealt with, and forgiven so that it will not be brought up against me ever again. When God forgives, He justifies. When God forgives, He credits Christ's righteousness to my account. When God forgives, He frees me from the guilt and penalty of my sin. This forgiveness by justification is almost unbelievable, so that's where faith comes in. What do the following verses have in common?

- **For therein is the righteousness of God revealed from faith to faith: as it is written, The just shall live by faith.** Romans 1:17
- **Even as Abraham believed God, and it was accounted to him for righteousness.** Galatians 3:6
- **But that no man is justified by the law in the sight of God, it is evident: for, The just shall live by faith.** Galatians 3:11
- **And the scripture was fulfilled which saith, Abraham believed God, and it was imputed unto him for righteousness: and he was called the Friend of God.** James 2:23

____

____

____

Romans 4 is all about Abraham. The Jewish community took a lot of pride in their ability to trace their lineage back to this Patriarch. Some even believed that by simply proving that they were direct descendants of Abraham that they would be ushered into heaven, no questions asked. They thought they were safe because they were children of Abraham. John the Baptist dealt with this in Matthew 3:1-6 and Luke 3:1-20 when he challenged the Pharisees and the Sadducees to prove by the way they lived that they had repented of their sins and turned to God. Turn to and read either the Matthew 3 or the Luke 3 passage to find the answer to this question: Knowing that justification is God's way of righteously dealing with our sin, why do you think John the Baptist's message of repentance was so important?

____

____

____

Some, in seeking to bring the concept of justification to an understandable level, have defined justification as, "Just as if we had never sinned." Even though this definition explains the meaning, it overlooks a very important thought. I am so very thankful that my sins have been forgiven, never to be brought up to me again, but I don't want to ever forget the wretchedness of my selfishness and sin in light of what God has done for me. Paul, in Romans 4:7-8, quotes David from Psalm 32:1-2, **Saying, Blessed are they whose iniquities are forgiven, and whose sins are covered. Blessed is the man to whom the Lord will**

not impute sin. In other words, what a joy it is to those who know that their sin is totally put out of sight, whose sinful record has been cleared of all guilt and Christ's righteousness has been put in its place. Explain when this happened to you personally. ______________

Paul spent a good deal of time dealing with the delicate issue of circumcision, explaining that it was not a work to gain acceptance by God, but a mark of identification for those who by faith trusted in God and desired an intimate relationship with Him. Abraham did nothing to earn righteousness before God or friendship with God. He simply believed. **He staggered not.** He did not doubt. He was **strong in faith**. He was **fully persuaded that, what God had promised, He was able to perform.** He believed that God could and would do the impossible by giving him (at 100) and his 99-year-old wife a child. (Can you imagine the looks they must have got walking through the market place when Sarah was about 8½ months pregnant?) Write out the rest of Romans 4:20-23 and take three minutes to meditate on these faith-packed words: **He staggered not at the promise of God.** ______

Therefore it is of faith, that it might be by grace (Romans 4:16). I must trust in the grace of God. Grace is a gift and therefore unmerited, undeserved, and unearnable. You can't buy it, earn it, steal it, or trade for it. It is a gift. A gift is not a gift if has to be paid for or earned. Romans 6:23 is a great verse that mentions both something earned and something given.
What is the wage (earnings) of sin? ______________
What is the gift of God through Jesus Christ? ______________

Now, although grace and eternal life are gifts from God, men have to "work" to receive God's wrath and judgment. They earn God's wrath by rejecting Him and **despising** (treating as worthless) **the riches of His goodness** (His grace) with their **hard and impenitent hearts** (Romans 2:4-5). Why do you think some choose to earn God's wrath rather than accept God's free gift of salvation? ______________

So, justification, which is all wrapped up in forgiveness and salvation, is the only answer for the sinful misery we studied in Romans 1-3. Man ruined his life in sin. God's remedy is Jesus Christ who gave His all that we may receive His all. Christ's righteousness was imputed to us so that God sees Christ's righteousness credited to our account. So, have you been justified? What does justification now mean to you?

Tuesday: Romans 5

Justification Experienced

jus·ti·fy, v. jus·ti·fied, jus·ti·fy·ing, jus·ti·fies

1. To demonstrate or prove to be just, right, or valid.
2. To declare free of blame; absolve.
3. To free (a human) of the guilt and penalty attached to grievous sin. Used of God.
4. In Christian theology, justification is God's act of reckoning a sinner righteous before God by the imputation of Christ's righteousness.

Have you ever received a huge care package full of all kinds of gifts? Once you open the bigger box it is almost like a birthday and Christmas all rolled into one. One by one, you open smaller wrapped packages and don't stop until you search the big box to make sure that you did not miss any. As we unpack Romans 5 (God's "care package"), we will see that it is full of many gifts as equally comforting and amazing as God's huge gift of justification. I wish we had time to study the intricacies of each gift, but we will only be able to glance at what's in God's care package. However, we have a lifetime to study each facet of each precious gift. Let's get unpacking.

Therefore being justified by faith, we have PEACE (5:1). Define peace: ________________

____

The word **peace** (*eirene*) occurs ninety-two times in the New Testament, ten of which appear in the book of Romans. Based on a sense of God's favor, it is the serene tranquility and eager acceptance of every situation (good or bad) and every person (pleasant or prickly) that God allows in your life. What two peace principles can you find in Philippians 4:7 and Colossians 3:15? ________________________________

____

____

List one sacred song or hymn that emphasizes God's peace. ________________________

____

Therefore being justified by faith, we have GRACE (5:2). Define grace: ________________

____

The word **grace** (*charis*) is almost too big to wrap your mind around. It is a divine enablement freely given as an expression of God's love and kindness to us. When at work, it enables, empowers, and encourages us to say "no" to sin and "yes" to God. It saves not just from the past penalty of sin, but from the present power of sin. When we accept God's grace, we will experience both the power and the desire to please Him. If someone asks you how the grace of God impacts your life, how would you use Philippians 2:13 and Hebrews 12:15 to answer their question? ________________________________

____

Therefore being justified by faith, we have HOPE (5:2-5). Define hope: ________________

____

I hope you can understand what hope is all about. **Hope** (*elpis*) is a confident expectation and a joyful anticipation of God's goodness. It may be the joyful anticipation of eternal life in heaven with all its wonders, joys, and opportunities to thank God for what He has done for us. Or, it might be the confident expectation that God is going to bring "good" out of a very difficult situation in life. Yesterday, we studied Romans 4:18-21. Read those verses again and explain what Abraham's **hope** rested in. ________________________________

____

Therefore being justified by faith, we have the HOLY SPIRIT (5:5). Describe what you think it means to be filled with the Holy Spirit:______________________________________

____

God's Spirit dwells in our spiritual hearts by faith for the purpose of comforting and convicting us. How could we either quench or grieve God's Spirit? ____________________

____

Therefore being justified by faith, we have the LOVE OF GOD (5:5). Describe the love of God:____

____

Love (*agape*) is often misunderstood. God's love is an undeserved, willful, affectionate care for us. God gives—not always what we want but always what we need. You have to love the literal meaning of the words **shed abroad**. The phrase "poured out" was used in the sacrificial system for the atonement of sin. Romans 5:6-9 describes the love that God **poured out** for us in the pouring out of Jesus' blood by which we sinners were **justified by** (the pouring out of) **His blood**. Got all that? How long has it been since you personally thanked God for saving you?____

Therefore being justified by faith, we have been RECONCILED TO GOD (5:10). Describe what it means to be reconciled to God: ____

____

The word **reconcile** (*katallatto*) conveys the idea of restoring a broken relationship to a healthy relationship. Because of our sin, we were considered **enemies** of God. Now, because of our reconciliation and justification, we are considered **friends** of God. How many of your friends know for sure that you are a "friend of God"? ____________________
How would they know that? ____

____

Who needs to know that? ____

Therefore being justified by faith, we are no longer viewed as **SINNERS** because of one man's disobedience **(ADAM)**, but are viewed as **RIGHTEOUS** because of one Man's obedience **(JESUS CHRIST)** as taught in Romans 5:12-21. When you put your faith in Jesus Christ and trusted Him and Him alone for the forgiveness of your sins, God no longer looked at you as a **sinner** outside of Christ, but as a **righteous** person because of Christ. Think about the gifts God listed for us in Romans 5. The righteous, who have been justified by faith, have received the gifts of peace, grace, hope, God's Holy Spirit, God's love, and the privilege of being reconciled to God Himself! That is a care package like no other. Now, those who reject God's goodness and look down on His grace will receive tribulation, anguish, indignation, and God's wrath as their earned, eternal wages. Take a minute to thank God for what He has given you. Thank God your spiritual care package. Isn't our Lord wonderful?

Wednesday: Romans 6

Sanctification: Our Position in Christ

Go to the Kentucky Derby and watch the jockeys maneuver for a better position. Visit a *NASCAR* race and hope that your favorite driver has earned the pole position (the starting position inside of the front row). When I wrestled in high school, I never wanted to be positioned flat on my back, for that is a very poor position to be in during a wrestling match. As a sinner, when I put my faith and trust in Jesus Christ's redemptive work, my position changed—for the better. Positionally, I was dead in sin; now I am alive to God! Positionally, I was a defeated slave to sin; now I am a victorious servant of God. My position in Christ (which I did nothing to receive) has changed everything. When God saved me and positioned me "in Christ," that was the beginning of His progressive sanctification process in my life. God is so good.

WANTED: DEAD OR ALIVE

Romans 6:1-11 explains that we are to consider ourselves "in Christ" both in His death and in His resurrection. Being positioned "in Christ" means that we are to be dead to the power of sin and alive to God! To the best of your ability, write down three major thoughts from these eleven verses. ______________________________

____

____

____

____

The entire chapter of Romans 6 could be divided into two simple thoughts as seen in Romans 6:11 and Romans 6:12. Romans 6:11 condenses the first eleven verses: **Likewise reckon ye also yourselves to be dead indeed unto sin, but alive unto God through Jesus Christ our Lord.** Consider yourself dead to sin! You don't have to sin anymore! Sin is not your boss and you can say "no!" Unless you live in the hills of the great Smoky Mountains, you probably have not used the phrase, "I reckon." See if you can list five synonyms for the word **reckon.**______________________________

____

____

If you listed words similar to consider, imagine, or think, you are on the right track. God's sanctification process involves thinking, thinking clearly, and thinking biblically. What three commands for biblical change do you find in Ephesians 4:22-24?

1. ______________________________
2. ______________________________
3. ______________________________

The renewing of the mind is essential for biblical change. Romans 6:11 shows us *how* to think and *what* to think. Our old flesh and sinful nature usually disagrees.

Reckon, think, consider yourselves dead to what? ______________________________

Reckon, think, consider yourselves alive to whom?______________________________

These young Roman Christians already knew that water baptism was a public display of their personal identification with Jesus' death, burial, and resurrection, testifying that they were totally immersed in Jesus Christ. If someone did not attend your baptismal service, how would they know that you are positioned, identified, and immersed "in Christ" today?

____

____

The answer to this question is found in our second half of this chapter which is summed up in Romans 6:12, **Let not sin therefore reign in your mortal body, that ye should obey it in the lusts thereof.** Both believers and unbelievers can observe what you are on the inside (the real you) by watching what or who you submit yourself to as king of your life! If one of your family members were asked who or what is the king in your life, what would they say? ______________________________

____

____

There are five reasons in the last eleven verses of Romans 6 that tell us why you should submit to God as your King instead of being enslaved to sin as your master.

• Because God has brought you from death to life! (6:13)
At salvation, you were united with Christ in His death, burial, and resurrection. You were in line to receive sin's wage (eternal death), but chose to step out of line, turn to Christ, and receive God's gift (eternal life). Write out Galatians 2:20. ______________________________

____

____

• Because you are under grace! (6:14)
Grace dethrones sin as Lord and replaces it with the Lord Jesus Christ. God's **grace** is the divine enablement to say "no" to the reign of sin. When Paul wrote to Titus, he reminded him that **grace** teaches us to deny what? (Titus 2:11-12)

____

____

____

• Because of the principle of bondage! (6:16)
Paul is trying to bring his readers back to their senses: "Don't you know, don't you understand, don't you realize that you will become the slave of whoever or whatever you choose to obey?" If sin is your master and lord, what do you have to look forward to in this life? ______________________________

____

____

If God is your Master and Lord, what do you have to look forward to in this life and all eternity? ______________________________

____

• Because this is a heart issue and it is in your heart to do so! (6:17-18)
Paul thanked God that these Roman Christians **obeyed from the heart**! This is huge! We can obey out of fear of what others will think about us, or we can obey from the heart because we simply love God. Do you obey God out of duty or devotion? Do you find yourself wanting to stay pure, control your tongue, and serve others because you "want to" or because you "have to"? ______________________________

____

• Because consequences are a result of life's choices! (6:21-23)
I trust that you have personally chosen God's free gift of salvation. When you are fruitful in this life, you need not be fearful about eternal life. Which are you today? ______________________________

____

Thursday: Romans 7

Sanctification: Our Problem With Sin

A quick read of Romans 7 both humbles me and reminds me that I am totally incapable of ever doing anything good! I have a friend who was raised in a certain Protestant denomination that taught that you had to earn your own salvation and do good things to gain God's favor. He tried. In fact, he tried hard by going to church, reciting religious phrases, and faithfully confessing his sin at confession. As a teen, he knew he could not be "good enough" to keep all the rules and regulations so he gave up. He knew that he could not keep all the "laws of the church" and assumed that he was destined to hell. In his early twenties, he heard the true gospel for the first time and accepted Christ as his Savior. He actually lived Romans 7-8 without even knowing that it was in the Bible. Now, read Romans 7 one more time.

We Christians have a problem dealing with our sinful flesh. It could seem hopeless. What do you do on a daily basis to control your flesh? ____________________________________

____

What do you do to change your flesh? ____________________________________

____

What do you do to conquer your flesh? ____________________________________

____

Paul came to a realization that every one of us needs to understand and admit. You can see the emotion in his statement, **O wretched man that I am! Who shall deliver me from this body of death?** (7:24) We are so wicked and so weak and it would be hopeless if we had to deal with our sin in our own strength. We need Romans 8! I can't be good enough (as explained in Romans 7), and I must depend on Christ and Christ alone to deliver me (as explained in Romans 8). Today we will concentrate on our need, our unworthiness, our sinfulness, our wickedness, and our inability to ever do anything good in ourselves.

PRETEND YOU ARE DEAD. (Romans 7:1-6)
Possums play dead. If a grizzly bear is attacking you, you had better play dead. To play dead you need to think dead and act dead. Dead people cannot talk, see, or think. They are dead!
Can a dead person ride a bike? Why not? ____________________________________
Can a dead person answer his cell phone? Why not? ____________________________
Can a dead person keep the law and do good? __________________________________

Five times in these six verses Paul uses the word **dead** to illustrate and explain how we should view our relationship with the law (doing good things to gain a good standing). What illustration did Paul use to explain this relationship with the law and why? __________

____

____

____

____

SEE HOW TERRIBLE YOUR SIN REALLY IS! (Romans 7:7-13)
God's law is not sinful, it simply shows me how sinful I am. Salvation is not a choice between heaven and hell, but between Jesus Christ and my sin. It is my sin that enslaves; it is my sin that controls; it is my sin that separates me from God. The more I understand

God's Word, the more I am aware of my incredibly wicked heart; the more I understand my sinful heart, the more thankful I am for what God has done for me. God's commandments are **holy, just, and good**. They reveal what I am, what I need, and how Christ can meet that need. Explain how the following commands are **holy, just, and good** for each one of us and those we would choose to sin against.

- **Honor thy father and thy mother.** (Exodus 20:12) ______________________________

____

- **Thou shalt not kill.** (Exodus 20:13) ______________________________

____

- **Thou shalt not commit adultery.** (Exodus 20:14) ______________________________

____

- **Thou shalt not steal.** (Exodus 20:15) ______________________________

____

If we did not have God's written laws, commandments, precepts, testimonies, statutes, and righteous judgments, we would not know that we were wretched sinners in need of a wonderful Savior. Do you view your sin in the same way that God views your sin? Write David's prayer from Psalm 139:23-24 and meditatively pray through this prayer asking God to reveal to you any unknown sin that may be in your heart. ______________________

____

____

____

WHAT A BATTLE! WILL IT EVER END? (Romans 7:14-25)

Have you ever stated something like this, "I don't get it! The things I hate to do, I do, and the things I should do, I don't do!" If so, join the club (and don't fret, Paul is part of our club too). The more you mature in Christ, the more you hate your sin. The more you grow in your sanctification process, the greater your abhorrence of the sin that holds you back from Christlikeness. What are two of the **good** things you know you should do, but struggle in both your consistency and commitment? ______________________________

____

____

What are two of the **evil** things you do, but wish you could stop doing? ______________

____

____

How can Ephesians 4:22-24 help you to mature in Christ and grow in your personal sancfication so that you start doing what you should do and stop doing what you should not do? ______________________________

____

O wretched man that I am! Who shall deliver me from the body of this death?

I thank God through Jesus Christ our Lord.

Friday: Romans 8

Sanctification: Our Power in Christ

As stated yesterday, we need Romans 8. We can't be good enough (as explained in Romans 7) and we must depend on Christ and Christ alone to deliver us (as explained in Romans 8). All Scripture is inspired by God. Some verses, because of their directness and clarity, seem to easily grab hold of our attention and are the ones often memorized and chosen as favorites. Romans 8 has at least ten of them. A quick meditation on each will encourage your heart to love your God even more.

There is therefore now no condemnation to them which are in Christ Jesus, who walk not after the flesh, but after the Spirit. Romans 8:1
For those of us who belong to Christ Jesus, who by faith have recognized our guilt before God and trusted in God's grace by accepting His forgiveness through Christ's death, who are not trusting in any good that we have done, but only what Christ has done for us, there is not one hint of condemnation. None! There is no condemning judgment against us. I have been forgiven and freed from the penalty of all my sin. God's forgiveness is a promise and He will never again rebuke us, criticize us, reprimand us, blame us, reprove us, or hold us accountable for that sin. Amen. How did Romans 8:1 encourage your heart today? ____

____

____

For ye have not received the spirit of bondage again to fear; but ye have received the Spirit of adoption, whereby we cry, Abba, Father. The Spirit itself beareth witness with our spirit, that we are the children of God: and if children, then heirs; heirs of God, and joint-heirs with Christ; if so be that we suffer with Him, that we may be also glorified together. Romans 8:15-17
I have a special relationship with God. It is not the relationship of a fearful slave but of a forgiven son. God adopted me! He chose me even though I did not deserve it. He is a loving Father that I can trust, depend on, and love with all my heart. This relationship involves His Spirit dwelling in me, affirming and assuring me that I am His child and someday (I can't wait) I will be in His presence sharing in all His glory. The difficult times of suffering because I am identified with Christ do not even compare with what God has for me in heaven some day. "Thank you, my wonderful God and loving Father." Explain how Romans 8:15-17 assures you of your salvation. ____

____

____

Likewise the Spirit also helpeth our infirmities: for we know not what we should pray for as we ought: but the Spirit itself maketh intercession for us with groanings which cannot be uttered. Romans 8:26
When I get so overwhelmed with my obvious weaknesses, infirmities, and helplessness, God's indwelling Spirit is there to help me, strengthen me, and even pray for me. There are times I just shake my head and don't know what to do or say. I can't even pray! That's when the Holy Spirit intervenes and intercedes for me by expressing my crushed heart's anguish

with groanings so deep that they cannot be expressed in words. What a wonderful God we have. Describe a time when you went to God in prayer, not even knowing what to pray, and just fell before Him. ____

____

____

And we know that all things work together for good to them that love God, to them who are the called according to His purpose. For whom He did foreknow, He also did predestinate to be conformed to the image of His Son, that He might be the firstborn among many brethren. Romans 8:28-29

All things—good or bad. **All things**—beneficial or difficult. **All things**—pleasureable or painful. Everything that happens in my life is designed to help me become more like Jesus Christ; this is God's good goal for me; this is God's purpose for my life; and all I need to do is to love my God more and more each day. I know I am called. I know my God is in control. I know that God has had a plan for my life for a long time. "Lord, help me to love you with my whole heart, soul, mind, and strength." What does Romans 8:28-29 mean to you personally?

____

____

____

Nay, in all these things we are more than conquerors through Him that loved us. Romans 8:37

Just because we have trouble or hard times or experience hunger, poverty, or even death threats does not mean that God does not love us. Despite all these things, we will be eternally victorious because of God's love to us. If God is for us, who can be against us? If God is for us, who can accuse us? God is for us. God loves us. Amazing! How does this verse help you get through a difficult day? ____

____

____

For I am persuaded, that neither death, nor life, nor angels, nor principalities, nor powers, nor things present, nor things to come, nor height, nor depth, nor any other creature, shall be able to separate us from the love of God, which is in Christ Jesus our Lord. Romans 8:38-39

I am convinced, I am persuaded, I am assured that nothing, absolutely nothing...

- neither death or life
- neither angels or demons
- neither present worries or future fears
- neither anything from the sky above or the earth below
- nothing in all of God's creation...including my own selfish heart

Nothing! Absolutely nothing can separate me from God's love that He revealed to me through the life, death, burial, and resurrection of His Son, Jesus Christ. Explain how you are persuaded of the same. ____

____

____

____

Saturday: Romans 9-11

Sovereignty: Our God Is in Control

I wish we had the time and the room in this Bible study to dig deeper into Israel's past election, present rejection, and future redemption as taught in Romans 9-11. There are teachings in this passage that are difficult to grasp and hard to understand. We must recognize that God has some mysteries and secrets that He is certainly entitled to. If I could totally understand the dynamic tension between God's sovereignty and man's free will, I would be God. I am not God and am more than willing to trust Him as a fair, just, loving, kind, and sovereign God. I think this is why God inspired Paul to end this second section of Romans in this way.

O the depth of the riches both of the wisdom and knowledge of God!
How unsearchable are His judgments, and His ways past finding out!
For who hath known the mind of the Lord? Or who hath been His counsellor?
Or who hath first given to Him, and it shall be recompensed unto Him again?
For of Him, and through Him, and to Him, are all things:
to Whom be glory for ever. Amen.
Romans 11:33-36

What can we learn from Israel's past election by God? (Romans 9:1-33)
Read Romans 9. I really cannot summarize the truths of Romans 9 any better than commentator Warren Wiersbe has in his *Expository Outlines on the New Testament*.

> Paul's purpose in this chapter is to explain Israel's position in the plan of God. Israel was an elect nation, given privileges that no other nation had; yet it failed miserably to follow God's program of blessing for the world. The entire chapter exalts the sovereign grace of God without minimizing the responsibility of men and women for making right decisions. God's Word will prevail regardless of human disobedience; but disobedient sinners will miss the blessing.[2]

You can't read through this passage without realizing that we have a wonderful and powerfully sovereign God who is in control. It is hard to understand why anyone would want to reject God's offer of redemption. Paraphrase Paul's sorrowful heart as he explained it in Romans 9:1-5. ____

____

____

____

____

____

Although God's election is difficult to grasp in our finite minds, we do know that according to Romans 9:14, we are never to accuse God of being unrighteous or unfair. No man, woman, or teen "deserves" to be forgiven and saved from their sin. If you have experienced God's forgiveness, it should humble you until all you can say to God is, "Thank You, thank You, thank You." In the box provided on the next page, briefly write a thank-you note to God expressing your gratitude for His free gift of salvation that you have received.

What can we learn from Israel's present rejection of God? (Romans 10:1-21)
Paul loved his people and wanted them to have a right relationship with God—God's way. God's way is simple; God's way must be shared with sinners; God's way is the only way—but available for all who will believe. Write out the following verses.

Romans 10:9-10 ______________________________

____

____

Romans 10:13 ______________________________

____

From these three verses, explain God's simple plan of salvation. ______________________________

____

____

____

If you want to call biblical Christianity a religion, there are only two religions in the entire world. Getting right with God through "works" is one and getting right with God through "faith" is the other. No one will ever get to God by being good enough—it will never happen. Everyone can get to God by trusting Jesus Christ who can and will forgive all sins for those who believe. As a whole, the nation of Israel rejected God's way, and therefore rejected eternity with God. Who do you know that has made the same choice? __________

____

What can we learn from Israel's future redemption by God? (Romans 11:1-36)
God is a merciful God. He wants Israel as a whole to repent and believe the gospel. He is both kind and severe in His treatment of those who hear the truth of the gospel: kind to those who believe the truth and severe to those who reject it. His mercy is available for all (Jew or Gentile) who will believe. After reading through Romans 9-11 today (not an easy read), list two questions that come to your mind that you cannot seem to understand what God has done, is doing, or will do with Israel. ______________________________

____

God has a plan and no matter who rejects His plan or seeks to change it, He will accomplish it in His sovereignty and timing. This should make us sing with Paul.

O the depth of the riches both of the wisdom and knowledge of God!
How unsearchable are His judgments, and His ways past finding out!
For who hath known the mind of the Lord? Or who hath been His counsellor?
Or who hath first given to Him, and it shall be recompensed unto Him again?
For of Him, and through Him, and to Him, are all things:
to Whom be glory for ever. Amen.

Sunday Review and Meditation

"Lord, O how great is Your forgiveness, grace, and mercy to justify an undeserving sinner like me!"

Justification Examined

Read Monday's study, define justification, and explain how it has impacted your life.

Justification Experienced

Read Tuesday's study and list as many of God's gifts that come from justification that you can remember.

Sanctification: Our Position in Christ

Read Wednesday's study and list three reasons why we should not allow sin to reign in our lives.

Sanctification: Our Problem With Sin

Read Thursday's study and write one paragraph explaining how God will help control, change, and conquer your flesh.

Sanctification: Our Power in Christ

Read Friday's study and explain one of the six principles from Romans 8 in your own words.

Sovereignty: Our God Is in Control

Read Saturday's study and write one paragraph explaining how God's wisdom and knowledge is totally unsearchable.

Section 3

Man has ruined his life in sin.
(Romans 1-3)

God's remedy is in Jesus Christ.
(Romans 4-11)

Therefore, how can I show my thankfulness to God for such deliverance?
(Romans 12)

Therefore

Man has ruined his life in sin.

We learned in our first week's study how depraved and wicked man's heart can become when he refuses to listen to God and pushes Him out of his life. When God is rejected and despised, evil reigns. The answer to such a wicked, depraved, sinful heart is the rescue, redemption, and reconciliation through Jesus Christ.

God's remedy is in Jesus Christ.

As we hurried through Romans 4-11 in our second section of this study, we learned that God's remedy to man's ruined life in sin is found in the life, death, burial, and resurrection of Jesus Christ. Being justified and sanctified in Christ gives us the special privilege to have our sins forgiven and experience a right relationship with the one and only true God.

Therefore, how can I show my thankfulness to God for such deliverance?

Romans 12-16 is full of practical principles and practices on how a forgiven sinner (now in Christ) should think, act, and live in a world of pride, strife, tension, hypocrisy, rebellion, evil, disobedience, lust, and a myriad of other sinful practices. Too many believers "forget" what God has done for them. It would take another six months to deal with all that God has listed for us in Romans 12-16, so we are going to take the next four weeks and concentrate on Romans 12 alone. Even then, twenty-four days in Romans 12 will only allow us to get through the first layer of this multi-layered, principle-packed passage of Scripture. Reading the chapter each day for the next four weeks will hopefully help in your meditation, memorization, and application of this life-changing passage.

Monday: Romans 12

Understand Paul's "therefore."

Therefore...Paul's "therefores" are always there for a specific reason. Whenever we find the word "therefore," we must look back and see what it is there for. A **therefore** in Scripture is a carabiner of truth often connecting a specific cause with a desired effect. Many commentators compare the relationships between doctrine and duty, belief and behavior, doctrinal teaching and exhortational preaching. As mentioned earlier in our study, the Heidelberg Catechism summarizes the book of Romans in three simple statements as it seeks to answer the question, "How many things does a person have to know in order to live and die a happy, contented, and fulfilled life?" Only three!

One: How great are my miseries and sin (Romans 1-3)
Two: How I can be delivered from my misery and sin (Romans 4-11)
Three: How I am to be thankful to God for such deliverance (Romans 12)

One: What has God saved you from? Describe the seriousness of your sinful condition before God reconciled you to Himself. ______________________________

____

____

____

Two: What did God do to save you from your miserable sins, justify you, and put you in a right relationship with Himself? ______________________________

____

____

____

Three: What should be your spiritual, reasonable, rational, sensible, logical, commonsensical response to God for His forgiveness and redemption? ______________________________

____

____

____

____

I am personally being mentored by some men whom God has gifted with incredible understanding of His Word. Although, I've never sat down in a coffee shop with any of these guys, they have shared their hearts in print (some hundreds of years ago) for me to learn from. Hopefully, during the millennial reign, I will be able to thank them personally for what they have done for me (maybe even in a coffee shop over a latte). Read each mentor's comments and write down a couple of thoughts for each one.

THEREFORE...from the viewpoint of Donald Grey Barnhouse

> The "therefore" of chapter twelve must look back over all the epistle and divide its revelation under two heads: (1) man's complete ruin in sin, and, (2) God's perfect remedy in Christ. Sin and salvation—this is the burden and the joy of the gospel, and this is the foundation for the practical, day-by-day Christian life.[3]

____

____

____

____

THEREFORE...from the viewpoint of Warren Wiersbe

In the Christian life, doctrine and duty always go together. What we believe helps to determine how we behave. It is not enough for us to understand Paul's doctrinal explanations. We must translate our learning into living and show by our daily lives that we trust God's Word. If we have a right relationship to God, we will have a right relationship to the people who are a part of our lives. "If a man say, I love God, and hateth his brother, he is a liar." (1 John 4:20)[4]

THEREFORE...from the viewpoint of William Hendriksen and Simon Kistemaker

What the apostle is saying is that in view of God's mercy, a voluntary and enthusiastic response of gratitude is required. What he is saying, then, is that this sovereign divine mercy calls for a life of complete dedication and wholehearted commitment. Animal sacrifices will not do! Nothing less than thorough self-surrender out of gratitude is required. What the apostle is teaching, therefore, is that Christian ethics is based on Christian doctrine. Returning once more to the opening chapters of Paul's epistle to the Romans and from there quickly reviewing the remainder of this precious writing, one cannot help becoming aware of the fact that in 1:1-3:20 man's sin and misery are described; in 3:21-11:36 the way of deliverance is opened to him; and in 12:1-16:27 the rescued believer is shown how, by a life of gratitude to God and helpfulness toward God's children and, in fact, toward everybody, man should respond.[5]

THEREFORE...from the viewpoint of Joseph Hall

Doctrine without exhortation makes men all brain, no heart; exhortation without doctrine makes the heart full, but leaves the brain empty. Both together make a man, one makes a wise man, the other a good man; one serves that we may know our duty, the other that we may perform it. Men cannot practice unless they know, and they know in vain if they practice not.[6]

THEREFORE...from the viewpoint of the Psalmist David in Psalm 50:15

MISERY: **Call upon Me in the day of trouble;**
DELIVERANCE: **And I will deliver you;**
GRATITUDE: **And you will glorify Me.**

"Thank You, Lord, for showing me my miseries and sin.
Thank You, Lord, for delivering me from my misery and sin.
Therefore, show me how I can daily please You
in my relationships with others and with You."

Tuesday: Romans 12

Understand God's mercies.

I beseech you therefore, brethren, by the mercies of God, that ye present your bodies a living sacrifice, holy, acceptable unto God, which is your reasonable service. And be not conformed to this world: but be ye transformed by the renewing of your mind, that ye may prove what is that good, and acceptable, and perfect, will of God.
Romans 12:1-2

I beseech you therefore, brethren, by the mercies of God
What do you do if you **beseech** someone?______________________________________

____

Paul is a great beseecher. We don't **beseech** as much as we should, although some **beseech** and don't even know it. Comparative translations use words such as plead, urge, or appeal. Without understanding the full intent of the word, it could come across as a begging of sorts. *The Complete Word Study Dictionary of the New Testament* explains that it means to aid, help, comfort, or encourage. Translated: to comfort, exhort, desire, or call for.[7] *The Exegetical Dictionary of the New Testament* translates it with the words request, urge, and comfort.[8] If **beseech** were a fruit, it would be a type of passion fruit growing on a compassion-care tree. The word used for **beseech** (*parakaleo*) actually comes from two Greek words: *para*, meaning "alongside of," and *kaleo*, meaning "to call." Paul was giving an encouraging, passionate appeal to do what he was already doing. He was basically saying, "Christian brother, come here by my side and together we will spend our lives thanking God for His unsearchable mercy that we have seen in Jesus Christ who paid the penalty for our sinful wickedness. God made a way for us to have a right relationship with Him."

Finish this phrase: "People don't care how much you know until they know ____________

____."

Paul was not asking anyone to do anything that he was not already doing himself. He was not harsh or demanding in his request. He did not authoritatively say, "Go sacrifice and do something for God!" He humbly requested, "Come with me, and we will serve our wonderful Lord together." Whether you are a parent, friend, brother, sister, teacher, pastor, counselor, or employer, how do you lead others? (By the way, we are all leaders. By our examples we are either leading others closer to God or farther from God.) In the past couple months, explain who you have influenced in their walk with God.______________

____

____

I beseech you therefore, brethren, by the mercies of God
Paul would write **brethren**; we would write brothers, sisters, or believing friends. This is not an evangelistic endeavor, but a godly man overwhelmed with God's mercies urging his believing friends to give their lives to God. God wants us to reach out to the unsaved as soul-winners, but He also wants us to reach out to wandering believers as soul-rescuers. List five Christian brothers or sisters (**brethren**) that need some encouragement to draw closer to the Lord.____

____

____

Often in the gospels, Jesus referred to the disciples as **brethren**. In the book of Acts, Peter, Stephen, and other preachers addressed "**men and brethren**" knowing that all men are not brothers, but all men could be brothers if they trusted in the same heavenly Father. In the thirteen letters that Paul wrote to his young, believing friends (we call them epistles), Paul referred to **brethren** over one hundred times...nineteen times in the book of Romans alone! Paul wrote letters. We send texts and e-mails. Paul prayed to discern the specific needs of his **brethren** and then addressed those issues. What do you do (or should you do) to encourage those five brethren you mentioned above to walk closer to God? ___________

____

____

____

I beseech you therefore, brethren, by the mercies of God

We all need to be daily reminded of God's **mercies. By the mercies of God** is Paul's credibility clause as he refers to Romans 1-11. God's **mercies** are almost unbelievable when you realize that these **mercies** are based on pity, love, and compassion to selfish, unloving, hard-hearted recipients. Paul reminds us in his second letter to the Corinthians that God is not only the **God of all comfort** but also the **Father of mercies**. When it comes to comfort or compassion, bypass the chain of command, skip the managers, the administrators, the CFO, COO, and CEO...go directly to our Father God! List three ways that God has been merciful to you.____

____

____

____

The opposite of God's mercy is God's wrath. To put a little reverential fear and true thankfulness in your heart, paint a picture of these two attributes of God and compare the implications of each: one deserved—the other undeserved; one petrifying in God's justice—the other overwhelming in God's goodness; one to fear—one to enjoy; both are of God and both will be seen in their ultimate fashion when God chooses to fulfil the promises of His prophetic Word. John Stott wrote, "There is no greater incentive for holy living than a contemplation of the mercies of God."[9] For a minute, meditate on Lamentations 3:22-23 and then express your thankful heart to God.

It is of the Lord's mercies that we are not consumed, because His compassions fail not. They are new every morning: great is Thy faithfulness.

____

____

____

____

Wednesday: Romans 12

Understand sacrificial living.

I beseech you therefore, brethren, by the mercies of God, that ye present your bodies a living sacrifice, holy, acceptable unto God, which is your reasonable service. And be not conformed to this world: but be ye transformed by the renewing of your mind, that ye may prove what is that good, and acceptable, and perfect, will of God.
Romans 12:1-2

That ye present your bodies

Paul is encouraging both his friends in Rome and his future friends that he will meet in the millennium (that's you and me) to **present your bodies**. How do you do that? Does it mean that you wrap your body up in Christmas wrap and give it as a present? Does it mean that if God calls roll you respond with, "Present"? Do you formally hand your body over to God in a public presentation? What do you think Paul is referring to when he asks those of us who are overwhelmed with God's mercies to **present our bodies**? ____________________

____

According to *The Complete Word Study Dictionary,* **present** (*paristemi*) comes from two words: *para*, meaning near, and *histemi* meaning to stand near or before.[10] *Thayer's Greek Lexicon* defines the word **present**: to bring into one's presence, to stand by, to be present.[11] Sometimes, it helps to understand a principle by examining its opposite. The opposite of *paristemi* is *aphístemi*: to depart or withdraw, to be absent, to remove oneself, to forsake, to desert. According to James 4:6-10 (turn there and read it), what would cause us to depart or withdraw from God's presence? ____________________

____

____

The word "deserter" carries a picture of a regretful, beaten-down, fearful failure traveling from town to town trying to escape the embarrassing memories of the past and the fear of future humiliation when he is found out for who he is once again. We have a choice to make. We can be as close to God as we want to be! In a way, we should wrap up ourselves as a present to God and when He calls our name, we can immediately say, "Here! Right by your side! Present!" Paul reminds us that this presenting (the willing desire to be close to God) is not just a spiritual thing, but we are also to present **our** physical **bodies**. Your body is that thing you live in; that thing you have to feed to keep alive; that thing that needs to be clothed to stay warm; that thing that needs sleep and rest at times; that thing that you spend hours painting and working on to look like a good thing before other things; that thing that gets you from place to place; that thing that is recognized by other things; that thing that is made of primarily dust and water and will someday return to such; that thing you call your body! In what way can you present your body to God as a spiritual sacrifice to God? ____________________

____

These corresponding verses may help. Read each passage and try to explain and apply what they have to say about both **your bodies** and your walk with God.

And the very God of peace sanctify you wholly; and I pray God your whole spirit and soul and body be preserved blameless unto the coming of our Lord Jesus Christ.
1 Thessalonians 5:23

____

____

What? Know ye not that your body is the temple of the Holy Ghost which is in you, which ye have of God, and ye are not your own? For ye are bought with a price: therefore glorify God in your body, and in your spirit, which are God's.
1 Corinthians 6:19-20 ______________________________

____

Let not sin therefore reign in your mortal body, that ye should obey it in the lusts thereof. Romans 6:12 ______________________________

____

That ye present your bodies a living sacrifice, holy, acceptable unto God

What kind of sacrifice is Paul asking for? A living sacrifice. A holy sacrifice. An acceptable sacrifice. A sacrifice that pleases God. What is **sacrifice**? **Sacrifice** is the willingness to give up something you love and cherish very deeply and is very valuable to you. Leviticus 1 describes the type of sacrifice that truly pleased God:

- It was sacrificing something very valuable (*without blemish*); it was sacrificing something that could bring greater wealth or prosperity in the future. (1:3)
- It was a willing, un-manipulated, right-from-the-heart sacrifice (*own voluntary will*). (1:3)
- It was a God-focused sacrifice (*before the Lord*). (1:3, 5)
- It was a personal this-is-for-my-sin sacrifice (*he shall put his hand on the head of the burnt offering*) (Note: the personal pronouns "he" or "his" are used eleven times). (1:4)
- It was a difficult sacrifice: to take the life of that innocent calf or lamb which was dying for me, for my sin, and for no other reason. (1:5)

I have to ask myself if I sacrifice to God with the same God-ordered mind-set that pleased Him so many years ago. Do I sacrifice anything that actually costs me something (or do I simply give out of my reserve)? Do I sacrifice because I want to (or because I feel like I have to)? In what way do you sacrifice to God? ______________________________

____

Which is your reasonable service (rational worship)

Reasonable (*logikeen*) means it is a rational choice. It is a "thinking" kind of worship which is missing from the forced liturgy of a denominational worship or the Baptist been-there-done-that-here-we-go-again worship. It is a kind of worship that has nothing to do with the pilgrimage of a Muslim, the mandatory suffering of a Buddhist, the ritualism of a Roman Catholic, or the constrained church attendance of a Baptist. It is a rational reasoning based on the infinite mercy of a gracious God. Habituated worship must be thought through. Always remember that Christianity is to be focused on Christ and not on Christians. How are your worship services on Sundays "thought through" in a way that forces you to concentrate on Christ and what He has done for you? ______________________________

____

____

" Lord, my commitment to You is my simple way of saying, Thank You!"

Thursday: Romans 12

Understand worldly conformity.

I beseech you therefore, brethren, by the mercies of God, that ye present your bodies a living sacrifice, holy, acceptable unto God, which is your reasonable service. And be not conformed to this world: *but be ye transformed by the renewing of your mind, that ye may prove what is that good, and acceptable, and perfect, will of God.* Romans 12:1-2

And be not conformed to this world

Paul challenges us with a tremendous goal in Romans 12:1. Now in verse 2, he tells us how to accomplish that goal. As one commentator put it, he shows us what *should be shunned* and what *should be done*. Before we dig in and dissect each of these words, what is your understanding of this well-known phrase, **be not conformed to this world**? ____________

____

____

____

____

And: The word **and** is a very important conjunction connecting two very important Bible principles. The **and** here reminds us that Paul is not finished explaining our "devotion-driven duty" due our wonderful Lord. He also wants us to realize that our willing, sacrificial commitment to Christ is to be couched in a non-conformist mind-set. Along with the positive encouragement to willingly and sacrificially commit to God, there is a negative admonition to not **conform** to this present age.

Be not: Don't continue to be; be being no longer; refuse to allow yourself. Stop it! No more! **Be** is an action verb. Action is the enemy of apathy. Just as we should be determined to do right, there are some things that we should passionately refuse.

What one word does Colossians 3:23 use to defy apathy? ____________________

In Psalm 119:10, what kind of heart should seek God? ____________________

According to Ecclesiastes 9:10, how should we do what we do? ____________________

And be not conformed

You don't have to "think" in order to conform. Like JELL-O®, you just simply ooze into the desired mold. You don't have to "think" to copy someone's behavior. Like art class in second grade, you just put a thin piece of white paper over your picture and start tracing. You don't have to "think" to follow worldly patterns, you just mimic what you see without thinking about how you get there or where it will lead you. Peter and Paul understood the danger of melting into a worldly mind-set. Both writers use the same word, although in Romans 12:2, Paul's *suschematizo* is translated **conformed** and in 1 Peter 1:14 Peter's *suschematizo* is translated **fashioning**. Whether it is the width of a belt, the style of hair, or the length of an outfit, the world's fashions change. The only thing constant about today's fashions is change. Again, to stay in style, you don't have to "think" on your own; just copy what everyone else is doing (whether it is good or bad); just mimic others. Why could this non-thinking approach to life be so dangerous? ____________________

____

____

____

And be not conformed to this world

Paul narrows the focus a little bit more as he tells us what to shun. Believers should be non-conformists in relation to the external, non-lasting, fleeting philosophy of the age we live in. Don't let the word philosophy scare you. It simply means, why we do what we do! When Paul talks about **this world,** it is much more than what we wear, what we listen to, and how we are entertained (although, all three of these issues are determined by how we much we are conformed to this world's way of thinking). Those without Christ and His Word think differently than those who are committed to Christ. Quickly compare the following issues from the world's mind-set and a biblical view.

Submission to authority (Romans 13:1; Ephesians 5:18-23; 1 Peter 5:5)

____

____

Moral purity (1 Thessalonians 4:1-5; Proverbs 5-7; 1 Corinthians 6:15-20)

____

____

Lying, cheating, and deceit (Proverbs 2:22; John 8:44; John 14:6)

____

____

Murder and abortion (Exodus 20:13; Galatians 5:19-21; Matthew 5:21-22)

____

____

As you can see, the world approaches most issues much differently than those who are committed to God's Word. The Apostle John's description of the world's mind-set (the way the world thinks) has not changed since he penned 1 John 2:15-17.

> **Love not the world, neither the things that are in the world. If any man love the world, the love of the Father is not in him. For all that is in the world, the lust of the flesh, and the lust of the eyes, and the pride of life, is not of the Father, but is of the world. And the world passeth away, and the lust thereof: but he that doeth the will of God abideth for ever.**

List five observations of how John describes the world's way of thinking.

1. ____
2. ____
3. ____
4. ____
5. ____

Remember, it's easy to conform (just refuse to think). Being a non-conformist to the world (refusing to think like the world thinks) is just another way to thank our wonderful Lord for His love, forgiveness, and grace to us.

Friday: Romans 12

Understand God's transformation.

I beseech you therefore, brethren, by the mercies of God, that ye present your bodies a living sacrifice, holy, acceptable unto God, which is your reasonable service. And be not conformed to this world: but be ye transformed by the renewing of your mind, *that ye may prove what is that good, and acceptable, and perfect, will of God.* Romans 12:1-2

But be ye transformed by the renewing of your mind
As a child, I dreamed of being a cowboy, a pioneer explorer, and a professional baseball player, but never an English grammarian. Wrestling with dangling participles, verb tenses, and adverbial phrases was not my favorite sport. (Now I wish I knew more.) Therefore, I need to borrow brains from guys like Hendriksen and Kistemaker (*New Testament Commentary Series*) who can help explain difficult Bible passages.

1. Paul uses the present tense: "Continue to let yourselves be transformed." Accordingly, this transformation must not be a matter of impulse: on again, off again. It must be continuous.
2. The verb used is in the passive voice. Paul does not say, "Transform yourselves," but "Let yourselves be transformed." Transformation is basically the work of the Holy Spirit. It amounts to progressive sanctification. (2 Corinthians 3:18)
3. Nevertheless, the verb is in the imperative mood. Believers are not completely passive. Their responsibility is not canceled. They must allow the Spirit to do His work within their hearts and lives. Their duty is to cooperate to the full. (Philippians 2:12-13)[12]

So, an understanding of the present tense, the passive voice, and the imperative mood gives us a solid hold on Paul's intent to both these young Romans and us. When it comes to a renewed mind and a transformed life, we need to get serious about our daily submission to the Holy Spirit's work in our lives. Knowing that God promises to do His part (transformation), what is our part? ______________________________
Let's dig into these two life-changing principles and see what God has for us today.

Be ye transformed
The word used for **transformed** in the Greek is *metamorphoo* which of course reminds us of our science term *metamorphosis*. What is the first thing that comes to your mind when you hear the words *transform* or *metamorphosis*? ______________________________

____

____

Being **transformed** is becoming something completely different from what you are. Interestingly, the root of this word is used only four times in our Bible: once here in Romans 12:2; once in 2 Corinthians 3:18; and twice in reference to Christ's transfiguration in Matthew 17:2 and Mark 9:2. When Christ was transfigured in the presence of Peter, James, and John, Matthew tells us that He **was transfigured before them: and His face did shine as the sun, and His raiment was white as the light.** Right before these fishermen's eyes Christ's earthly body was transformed to a heavenly body. His supernatural body glistened brightly and glowed like the blinding sun. It was a dramatic, visible change. Obviously, you don't walk around with a glowing halo over your head, but what visible change can others see in you since you yielded your life completely to Christ? ______________________________

____

____

Paul encourages us in the transformation process when he wrote, **but we all, with open face beholding as in a glass the glory of the Lord, are changed into the same image from glory to glory, even as by the Spirit of the Lord** (2 Corinthians 3:18). In other words, we are being transformed into the likeness of Jesus Christ day-by-day and step-by-step through the power of the Holy Spirit of God! From this verse, what does God reveal about His power and His patience with us?____

____

____

God transforms us for His glory as we seek to biblically renew our minds.

By the renewing of your mind

There is no pill you can take for this. The **renewing** of the **mind** will never be accomplished with five minutes of prayer or drive-through-devos each morning. The renewal process is a minute-by-minute, hour-by-hour, day-by-day, week-by-week, month-by-month, year-by-year discipline. This must be our life practice. What have you already learned in life about **renewing your mind**?____

____

Who wants a stale, musty, out-of-date, worn out, tired, grumpy, grouchy old mind? To renew is to make new again. The newness of a baby's mind with its innocence, purity, intense desire to learn, and uncorrupted thinking process is something to envy. If we can somehow clean out the entertainment garbage, the selfish reasonings, and the worldly thought processes, we would be on our way to both a renewed mind and a transformed life. To remodel an old house, you need to get rid of the old and replace it with new. In your mind, you need to replace hate with what? Lust with what? Anger with what? Fear with what? Selfishness with what? Pride with what? Laziness with what? What does Colossians 3:10 say the **new man** is renewed in?________________________________

____

How does 2 Corinthians 4:16 say the **inward man** is renewed? ____________________

____

So, to remake, remodel, and make new the thoughts and attitudes of our selfish and immature minds, which verse above tells us that it will take a consistent, step-by-step commitment?____

Which verse reveals that we need to know more and more about our Creator, the Lord Jesus Christ? ____

What do you do on a daily basis to renew your mind?_____________________________

____

____

So, how can I thank God for delivering me from my sin? I must fervently renew my mind and watch my Lord transform my life into a life that pleases Him.

Saturday: Romans 12

Understand God's will.

I beseech you therefore, brethren, by the mercies of God, that ye present your bodies a living sacrifice, holy, acceptable unto God, which is your reasonable service. And be not conformed to this world: but be ye transformed by the renewing of your mind, that ye may prove what is that good, and acceptable, and perfect, will of God. Romans 12:1-2

That ye may prove what is that good, and acceptable, and perfect, will of God
As we become less and less conformed to this world and more and more transformed into the likeness of Jesus Christ Himself, we will be more able to discern God's will for our lives and more prepared to display to others that the will of God is perfect, acceptable, and very, very good. To the best of your ability, what is God's will for your life? ____________________

____

Discerning the will of God takes some effort. You will not find it in a fortune cookie at your favorite Chinese restaurant, by flipping a coin, or written on your Facebook wall. In fact, if you have not applied what we learned the last couple days (refusing to accept the world's way of thinking and instead, renewing and saturating your mind with Scripture) you will probably have a hard time discerning God's will for your life. Explain how Ephesians 4:22-24 partners with Romans 12:1-2 in teaching God's threefold process of biblical change?

____

____

____

Many of us, after failing a difficult Algebra test or bombing an English grammar quiz, have considered quitting school. Now, if you quit the school of Scripture that talks about putting off selfish habits, or if you play hooky from the course on renewing your mind, you will never be able to pass the test of proving to yourself God's will for your life! Before we go on to discuss the three elements of God's will, explain how you are fulfilling the following spiritual obligations which are foundational in knowing and understanding the wonderful will of God.

- What are you doing daily to keep from being **conformed to this world**? ______________

  ____

  ____

- What are you doing daily to **renew your mind**? ______________________________

  ____

- How has God **transformed** your life in the last couple weeks? __________________

  ____

  ____

That good, and acceptable, and perfect will of God
Although some of God's will is concealed, much of it is revealed. We must make sure we are honoring the revealed will of God before we can confidently expect to know His concealed will. What does God's Word already say about God's will? There are actually over twenty New Testament references to the will of God. What does 1 Thessalonians 5:18 say is **the will of God**? ____

____

How does Paul refer to **the will of God** in 1 Thessalonians 4:3? ____________________

____

According to Ephesians 6:6, how should we do **the will of God**? ____________________

____

God is pleased with both a heart that desires purity and expresses thanksgiving. In a more general way, God's Word is God's will! Since God wants the best for our lives, He wants us to live according to His will (which is according to His Word). In Romans 12:2, Paul describes God's will with what three words?____________________

____

God's will is always **good**! In one word, it's profitable. Jesus spoke of **good** trees and **good** soil; Mary chose the **good** part at Jesus' feet; **good** things come from the heart of **good** men; **good** gifts come from a **good** God. Each use of the word **good** shows us something that is good as compared to bad, beneficial as compared to harmful, useful as compared to wasteful. God's will is always good! How has God already used your life's gifts for something **good** and how do you envision Him using your spiritual gifts for **good** in the future? _____

____

____

____

God's will is always **acceptable**! In three words, it's pleasing to God. Here is a short, concise, personal testimony from our Lord Jesus as He lived on this earth: **He that sent Me is with Me...for I do always those things that please Him** (John 8:29). Paul then testifies of Christ in Romans 15:3 when he wrote, **For even Christ pleased not Himself.** We can choose to either please God (which is acceptable) or please self (which is totally unacceptable). In what ways have you pleased God (walked in His will) or displeased God (run from His will) in the past two weeks?____________________

____

God's will is always **perfect**! In six words, it will produce God's intended purpose. The root word for perfect is *teleo* which has its own portfolio of word pictures. Meaning full, complete, or finished, *teleo* was used for Scripture in 1 Corinthians 13:10, for love in 1 John 4:18, for the mature believer in Colossians 1:28, and for Christ's final words on the cross, **"It is finished,"** in John 19:30. God has an intended purpose for your life that He wants to bring to a finish. Stay in His will and in His Word and watch Him accomplish His purpose in your life. To prove this, **be not conformed to this world but be ye transformed by the renewing of your mind.** What a wonderful way to thank God for His redemptive work in your life. He forgave you. He saved you. How are you faithfully living in God's good, acceptable, and perfect will? ____________________

____

"Thank You, Lord, for your good, acceptable, and perfect will!"

Sunday Review and Meditation

"Lord, thank You for saving me from my sin and delivering me from its consequences through Jesus Christ my Lord!"

Understand Paul's "therefore."

Read Monday's study and explain how the principles of Romans 12:1-2 have impacted your life.

Understand God's mercies.

Read Tuesday's study and explain how the truths of Romans 12:1-2 have challenged your life.

Understand sacrificial living.

Read Wednesday's study and explain how the teaching of Romans 12:1-2 has convicted you.

Understand worldly conformity.

Read Thursday's study and explain how the command of Romans 12:1-2 has altered your life.

Understand God's transformation.

Read Friday's study and explain how the confrontation of Romans 12:1-2 has made you think.

Understand God's will.

Read Saturday's study and explain how the exhortation of Romans 12:1-2 can change your life.

Monday: Romans 12

Think! Think! Think!

For I say, through the grace given unto me, to every man that is among you, not to think of himself more highly than he ought to think; but to think soberly, according as God hath dealt to every man the measure of faith. Romans 12:3

Now here's a verse that gives us (every one of us) something to **THINK** about. God has an assignment for each one of us and His purpose will be revealed through the grace-induced inner desires and giftedness He has given us. Different people think of different ways to handle different tasks. God has gifted (assigned) each one in His body the necessary gifts to fulfill the assigned tasks He has given. Not everyone is assigned the same task or gifted in the same way. No one task makes the doer any more special to God than another. We are to simply use the gifts and enablement that God has given us to do what He wants us to do. What do you think is God's assignment for your life and how are you preparing for or fulfilling His purpose?______________________________________

____

____

As Paul encourages us to stop and think (emphasizing what "not to think" and what we "ought to think"), he uses the root word *phroneo* four times in this forty-four word, God-inspired sentence. Think, think, think, think! Most of us are either too tired to think, too busy to think, too lazy to think, or are happy to let someone else think for us! "Just tell me what to do. Don't make me think!" But God wants us to think. How?

God tells us what we are **not to think** and what we **ought to think**.
But we are to **think** how He wants us to think...**think soberly**.

Not to think of himself more highly

We often pray, "Lord, I am nothing and worthless. Please use me in spite of me." Then when someone else calls us nothing or worthless, we get all bent out of shape. It might reveal that we are not being totally honest when we boast of nothingness to God! When we realize that any and every ability that we have has been gifted or given to us by God (that we did not deserve, earn, work for, or buy), how can there be any room for pride or arrogance? There are really no self-made men in the body of Christ. How can I get proud when it is all of God (through His grace) and none of me!

The Greek word *huperphronéo* comes from the words *hupér* (above or over) and *phronéo* (to think). It means to think highly, to consider something of great importance. Some think that they are Superman! Although they may not be faster than a speeding bullet or have the ability to leap tall buildings in a single bound, they do think they are "Super" in the sense of being superior to others who are not as gifted, talented, or exceptional as they are. Do you think you are more important to God than others? Do you think that because you are so special to God, that He loves you more than anyone else on earth? How do Acts 10:34 and 1 Peter 1:17 attack such haughty thinking?____________________________

____

Ought to think

We must think. It is necessary to think. It is inevitable to think once all the facts are in. How **ought** we to think about ourselves? Go back to our first week of study as we examined the gravity of depravity in Romans 1-3 and honestly evaluate your motives, your thought life, your selfishness, your attitudes, etc. What **ought** you think about yourself? ____________

____

Commentator Donald Grey Barnhouse encourages us, "Think meek! Meekness is a vertical virtue, measuring self against God at every moment. It has nothing to do with the horizontal virtue that measures a man by other men."[13] As we compare ourselves with a holy, wonderful God, we are reminded that **all have sinned** and fallen short of what, according to
Romans 3:23? ____
Compared with God's glorious perfection, we should be humbled to **not think of** (ourselves) **more highly than** (we) **ought to think; but to think soberly.**

But to think soberly

In the Greek New Testament, this phrase looks something like this: *allá phroneín eis tó sophroneín*. If you notice, the word *phronein* appears twice. Literally, Paul is telling us to think with thinking that is sober, sane, discreet, discerning, and self-disciplined. It is actually the opposite of foolish, insane, undisciplined thinking. We are what we think. What we are thinking today we are becoming tomorrow. If we can think the way that God wants us to think, then we will live according to God's good, acceptable, and perfect will for our lives. On the other hand, if we are controlled by undisciplined, irrational, and foolish thoughts, we will displease our wonderful Lord. On a scale of one to ten (one poor; ten great), how would you rate your thought life? ____
Specifically, God is reminding us to be totally honest in our self-appraisals. We can do this if we contemplate Paul's personal thoughts of himself: **Whereof I was made a minister, according to the gift of the grace of God given unto me by the effectual working of His power. Unto me, who am less than the least of all saints, is this grace given, that I should preach among the Gentiles the unsearchable riches of Christ** (Ephesians 3:7-8). Have you ever struggled with what the world calls a "low self image"? If so, how? ________

____

Don't be fooled with such thinking; remember, we are created by God, created in His image, created for His glory! Unreservedly we are given gifts by God! Look at the end of our verse: **according as God hath dealt to every man the measure of faith.** Let me repeat myself. God has an assignment for each one of us. His purpose will be revealed through His grace-induced inner desires and giftedness. God has gifted (assigned) each one in His body to fulfill the assigned tasks He has given. We are to simply use the gifts and enablement God has given to us to do what He wants us to do. So, seriously think. How are you fulfilling God's desire for your life? ____

____

____

"Lord, every day remind me to think, think, think, and then think some more!"

Tuesday: Romans 12

Accept who you are.

For as we have many members in one body, and all members have not the same office: so we, being many, are one body in Christ, and every one members one of another. Romans 12:4-5

We are all different. Very different! We have different gifts, different personalities, different backgrounds, different looks, different viewpoints, different opinions, different goals, and different dreams. We are all different because God created us that way. The infinitesimal creativity and variety in God's creation can be seen in the plant world, the creatures of the sea, the animal world, and our world of man. We are all created in God's image, but there is only one of Him and many of us. As you read and think through these two verses, write down two questions that come to mind.

1. ____

____

2. ____

____

Here are some other questions that we will try to deal with today and tomorrow.

1. Just how many members are in our bodies?
2. What is the purpose of some of the uncomely parts (big toes, nose hairs, etc.)?
3. Are any members of my body insignificant, unnecessary, or worthless?
4. Are any members of Christ's body insignificant, unnecessary, or worthless?
5. What is my role or responsibility (office) in Christ's body?
6. What is my responsibility to the other members of Christ's body?
7. Since there are so many members, who should be in charge?

Our bodies are made up of **many members** or parts. How many? Well it depends on how specific or general you want to be. If you want to count each chromosome, go for it, but you had better have plenty of free time because there are 46 chromosomes in each cell and humans have about 100 trillion cells, give or take a few. Jewish tradition, according to the Talmud, says that the Jew was given 613 commandments (called the mitzvoth): 248 positive commands and 365 negative commands. The 365 negative commands match the number of days in a year and some say that the 248 positive commands correspond to the number of parts of our body. Interesting. Did this just happen? List two Scripture passages that you run to when someone attempts to convince you that you "evolved" and were not created by God. ____

How could Genesis 1:1, 26; Isaiah 45:12, 18; John 1:3, 10; Colossians 1:16-17; and Revelation 4:11 help you explain your personal faith and position on creation?

____

____

____

____

Knowing that there are **many members** to our bodies, you have to wonder if we could do without any? Do we really need big toes, nose hairs, and an appendix? Some argue about the appendix, but it is a good hangout for good bacteria until it is needed. It would be hard to keep your balance without a big toe, and can you imagine the millions of ugly germs, spores, and pathogens that would fly up your nostrils without nose hairs? Nothing that

God has orchestrated in your body is worthless, unnecessary, or insignificant? And neither are you worthless to the body of Christ. Do you ever feel invisible or insignificant to God? If you do, how do you biblically attack those foolish thoughts? ______________________

____

____

____

Here is one more passage that is both comforting and convicting when we start to question why God made us the way He did or doubt that God even knows that we exist. Meditate on these precious words from God and share your thoughts below.

> **I will praise Thee; for I am fearfully and wonderfully made: marvellous are Thy works; and that my soul knoweth right well. My substance was not hid from Thee, when I was made in secret, and curiously wrought in the lowest parts of the earth. Thine eyes did see my substance, yet being unperfect; and in Thy book all my members were written, which in continuance were fashioned, when as yet there was none of them. How precious also are Thy thoughts unto me, O God! How great is the sum of them! If I should count them, they are more in number than the sand: when I awake, I am still with Thee.** Psalm 139:14-18

____

____

____

Just as the nose and toes have different functions to the body, so do you and I. The word **office** in Romans 12:4 has the concept of doing or performing a certain action. Synonyms such as role, function, job, responsibility, or task help us to understand its meaning. So, what is your **office** in the body of Christ? How has God gifted you to do your part? Where do you fit in to His master plan for mankind? ______________________________

____

If the world was divided into three categories—slackers, wannabes, and doers—where would you fit in? ____

How does God apply the following passages to slackers, wannabes, and doers?

Deuteronomy 6:5 ____

____

____

Ecclesiastes 9:10 ____

____

____

Colossians 3:23 ____

____

____

Remember, we are all different, and God made us that way. One way to thank God for rescuing us from our sin is to accept who and what we are and live for His glory.

Wednesday: Romans 12

Love one another.

For as we have many members in one body, and all members have not the same office: so we, being many, are one body in Christ, and every one members one of another. Romans 12:4-5

Yesterday, we dealt with **many members** and how all those members do **not have the same office**, role, or function in the body. Today let's consider two more questions that these two verses bring to mind. What is my responsibility to the other members of Christ's body? Since there are so many members, who should be in charge?

What is my responsibility to the other members of Christ's body?

When Paul wrote that **every one** of us were **members one of another**, God was not just filling space in His book with words. These words have a purpose that we cannot overlook or ignore. This phrase has the concept of all "belonging" to each other. I totally understand author Donald Grey Barnhouse's statement, "I minimize our differences in secondary matters and magnify the oneness that is ours because we have been taken out of the same pit, established on the same rock, and given the same song to sing."[14] But we also need to keep in mind the concept of biblical separation from those who are purposefully (or even without malice) violating scriptural principles—for unity's sake, or number's sake, or acceptance sake, or Pete's sake (whoever Pete is). The ultimate is God's glory and not unity. Even the Lord said that a commitment to Him will cause division in families. I need to be fully persuaded in my mind that what I commit to is of God and worth causing division. There will always be division between believers and unbelievers, but what about believing brothers? If I take a stand against a believing brother, I must be bottom-line, Bible-sure on those things. If I cannot be Bible-sure, I will still live it but won't insist that everyone has to agree with me.

God uses the phrase **one another** in many ways with varied applications. If we want to understand how Jesus Christ wants us to treat each other, study the one anothers.

What new commandment did Jesus give us in John 13:34-35? ____________________

____

According to Romans 12:10, how should brothers treat each other? ____________

____

What example did Jesus give us in Romans 15:7? ____________________

____

When those in Christ's body start to drift from God, what does Romans 15:14 admonish us to do? ____________________

Galatians 5:13 tells us to do what with love? ____________________

____

According to Ephesians 4:2, how are we to manifest patience? ____________

____

What do both Ephesians 4:32 and Colossians 3:13 encourage us to do? ____________

____

How should we use God's promises, according to 1 Thessalonians 4:18? ____________

____

Instead of tearing each other down with words, Jesus Christ wants every member of His body to do what, according to 1 Thessalonians 5:11? ____________________

____

I know we have already mentioned it, but the Apostle John (the apostle of love) had a true burden on his heart for each member of the body of Christ. What does John repeat over and over in 1 John 3:11, 23; 4:7, 11, 12; and 2 John 5? ____________________

____

What did Paul mean when he admonished the young converts in Galatia, **But if ye bite and devour one another, take heed that ye be not consumed one of another** (Galatians 5:15)? ____________________

____

Paul dealt with this very same issue with the young and struggling Corinthian believers telling them that there should be no division in the body but that the members should genuinely care for each other (1 Corinthians 12:25). Would Christ be pleased with the way you love, prefer, receive, admonish, serve, forbear, forgive, comfort, and edify both your agreeing and disagreeing brothers in Christ? If not, what should you do? ____________________

____

Since there are so many members, who is in charge?

Paul does not explain the headship of Christ in Romans 12, but it is necessary to remind ourselves that Christ is the head of the body and should be in control of each and every member; that no member should strive to have preeminence over any other members; and that if each member of the body is motivated by love, the body of Christ will mature and grow into a healthy, loving body. What do the two passages below teach us about Christ's role as the head of the body and our role as individual members in His body?

But speaking the truth in love, may grow up into Him in all things, which is the head, even Christ: from whom the whole body fitly joined together and compacted by that which every joint supplieth, according to the effectual working in the measure of every part, maketh increase of the body unto the edifying of itself in love. Ephesians 4:15-16 ____________________

____

____

____

And He [Christ] **is before all things, and by Him all things consist. And He is the head of the body, the church: who is the beginning, the firstborn from the dead; that in all things He might have the preeminence.** Colossians 1:17-18 ____________________

____

____

____

These things I command you, that ye love one another. John 15:17

Thursday: Romans 12

Thank God for His grace gifts!

Having then gifts differing according to the grace that is given to us, whether prophecy, let us prophesy according to the proportion of faith; or ministry, let us wait on our ministering: or he that teacheth, on teaching; or he that exhorteth, on exhortation: he that giveth, let him do it with simplicity; he that ruleth, with diligence; he that sheweth mercy, with cheerfulness.
Romans 12:6-8

Having then gifts differing according to the grace that is given to us

- We are all different, with different gifts and different abilities. God did that.
- God, by His grace, has given us different gifts to do certain things well.
- Our gracious God has enabled us with specific gifts. Let's use them for His glory!
- Focus on using your gifts and refuse to focus on the misuse of other's gifts.
- Remember, they are gifts—unearned and undeserved.

Before we try to unpack these truths, what do you already know about the Giver (God), the Giver's grace which enables us to use our gifts, and the specific gifts given to you through our wonderful Giver's grace? ____________________

____

____

The Gifts

James 1:17 reminds us that all good gifts come from God, our unchanging heavenly Father. A gift is just that. A gift! You don't work for a gift; you can't earn a gift; you never pay the giver back for a gift; you don't deserve a gift. God looked down over His entire church and knew what gifts were necessary to help them grow and mature in Christ. Describe how God uses these gifts to help His children grow and change.

prophesying ____________________

____

serving (minister) ____________________

____

teaching ____________________

____

encouraging (exhorteth) ____________________

____

giving ____________________

____

leading (ruleth) ____________________

____

showing mercy ____________________

____

The Giver

Actually, this is the second time Paul deals with God, grace, and gifts in this chapter. Just three verses earlier Paul encouraged us to **think soberly, according as God hath dealt to every man the measure of faith** (12:3). As we compare that phrase with **having then gifts differing according to the grace that is given to us** (12:6), and ask counsel from Peter, we get a better idea of what is being taught here. **As every man hath received the gift, even so minister the same one to another, as good stewards of the manifold grace of God. If any man speak, let him speak as the oracles of God; if any man minister, let him do it as of the ability which God giveth: that God in all things may be glorified through Jesus Christ, to whom be praise and dominion for ever and ever. Amen.** 1 Peter 4:10-11

God is the One who gives.
God is the One who chooses who gets what gift or how many gifts.
God is the One who enables the getter to use the gift that he got.
God is the One who should get the glory (and not the getter).

So, how does God graciously enabled you to serve Him? ________________________________

____

____

____

____

The Grace

Paul begins his warning to those gifted by God by saying, **For I say, through the grace given unto me**. He wanted all to know that he could not have written his prophetic, confrontive, exhortation to stay humble aside from the grace of God. It seems that some value certain gifts better than others and are proud if they have a "showier" gift. Why is it much easier to stay humble using the gifts of serving or giving than preaching and leading? ____

____

____

Now, the reason we have gifts, the reason we have different gifts, and the reason we have different degrees of different gifts is **according to the grace that is given to us**. Peter uses the phrase, **the manifold grace of God**, which could be translated God's varied grace, God's grace in various forms, or God's grace given in a multitude of colors (like the variegated yarn my grandma used to use which included every color in the rainbow). Don't worry about what color of a gift you got or how much of that gift you received, just use your giftedness to serve Christ and love others. Grace can be defined as divine enablement. God not only gives you the gift but the ability to use it properly. Write out Philippians 2:13 and apply it to God's grace and gifts. ____

____

____

____

A half-full, ten thousand-gallon tank looks much more impressive than a small pint jar that is full and running over. Don't let the size of the container impress you or discourage you. Determine what size tank or jar you are, commit it totally to the Lord, and let it overflow. As you spill all over the place, you will impact lives for God's glory.

Friday: Romans 12

Use your gifts for God!

Having then gifts differing according to the grace that is given to us, whether prophecy, let us prophesy according to the proportion of faith; or ministry, let us wait on our ministering: or he that teacheth, on teaching; or he that exhorteth, on exhortation: he that giveth, let him do it with simplicity; he that ruleth, with diligence; he that sheweth mercy, with cheerfulness.
Romans 12:6-8

Every believer is gifted by God. Some, through the habit of selfish thinking, may believe that they are incredibly gifted above all others, and others, still through habitual selfish thinking, believe that they have received no gifts from God. Both manifestations of selfish thinking are unbiblical and displeasing to God. God gifted you to serve Him in a unique and special way. Although Paul deals with other gifts and talents in Ephesians 4 and 1 Corinthians 12, he lists here seven gifts that God has given for the purpose of using godly people to help other people be godly.

Prophesying: let us prophesy according to the proportion of faith
Prophesy! Preach the Word! Give the Truth of God, with the love of God, so lives are changed for the glory of God. Speak out with as much faith as God has given, but no more. In answer to the question, "Who is Jesus?" in Matthew 21:10, the multitude said, **This is Jesus the prophet of Nazareth of Galilee.** In our endeavor to be like Christ, we must not ignore growing in this gift. There are two ways to look at **prophesying:** either it is a fore-telling of the truth or a forth-telling of the truth. Today, we have the complete, sufficient Word of God and do not need or should not seek "new" truth. Paul reminds us that true, modern-day **prophesying** must include three elements (1 Corinthians 14:3). List all three principles and explain how each aspect of true preaching (**prophesying**) should help congregations today.

- E______________________________

- E______________________________

- C______________________________

How should those gifted in **prophesying** apply 2 Timothy 4:2 to their lives? ____________

What does Romans 10:15 have to say about gifted preachers? ____________

What should be a preacher's goal according to Colossians 1:28? ____________

How does a person know if they are called or not called to preach God's Word?

Ministry (serving): **or ministry, let us wait on** (use our grace-gift in) **our ministering**
There are capital "M" ministers and little "m" ministers. Our Lord Jesus Christ came to earth as a little "m" minister. Write out Matthew 20:28. ______________________________

____

Jesus chose to be a servant. Philippians 2:2-8 describes the mind of a servant while John 13:4-17 illustrates the actions of a servant. Jesus willingly, joyfully, sacrificially, and humbly served. When you read through those passages you will realize that our Lord did not serve out of duty, guilt, or gain. Those who possess the gift of serving also possess character traits such as dependability, initiative, and perseverance. They seem to know what needs to be done and do it! They prepare the surroundings to make it easy for those preaching, teaching, or counseling to use their gifts without distractions. List three simple and practical ways to serve others in your church and then explain how dependability, initiative, and perseverance fits such service.

1. ____

____

2. ____

____

3. ____

____

Minister! Serve others well with a servant's heart. Serve because you want to and because you find joy in doing so, not because you have to.

Teaching: or he that teacheth, on teaching
Teach! Be fully prepared so that your students will not only learn, but will understand the biblical reasoning behind the knowledge you teach. Teach because you are driven to do so, not because you don't know what else to do. So far in life, what has been your teaching experience? What do you like and what scares you about teaching? ______________

____

____

Teaching is more than transmitting factual data from one person to another. God's three-fold plan of change in Ephesians 4 (Put off/Renew/Put on) involves being **renewed in the spirit of your mind** which is often accomplished through passionate and biblical teaching. Who are you presently helping to grow and change by teaching them to renew their minds?____

____

I love Donald Grey Barnhouse's comment on this gift in his *Exposition on Romans.*

> When you receive a blessing from the Word of God, pass it on at once. When you learn something from a sermon, tell two or three other people at the earliest possible opportunity. Above all, apply the teaching to your own heart first; thus it comes to the listener with the impact of Heaven and the warmth of your own experience.[15]

Don't forget the Holy Spirit's reproof to the Hebrew Christians in Hebrews 5 when He reminded them that they seemed slow in grasping spiritual truth and should have already been teaching others but were still struggling with the ABC's of God's Word. Let the Holy Spirit of God use the holy Word of God to teach you how to be holy so you can teach others to be holy also. Do you have this desire? ______________________________________

____

Prophesy! Serve! Teach! Use your God-given gift for a gift-giving God!

Saturday: Romans 12

Encourage others, give to others, and lead others in a merciful way.

Having then gifts differing according to the grace that is given to us, whether prophecy, let us prophesy according to the proportion of faith; or ministry, let us wait on our ministering: or he that teacheth, on teaching; or he that exhorteth, on exhortation: he that giveth, let him do it with simplicity; he that ruleth, with diligence; he that sheweth mercy, with cheerfulness.
Romans 12:6-8

Yesterday we discussed three of the seven gifts Paul mentions: God's purpose and plan for the prophet, servant, and teacher. It is interesting to note that our Lord Jesus Christ possessed all three of those gifts along with the four we will study today. So, as we strive to be like Christ, we should also grow in each gift.

Or he that exhorteth, on exhortation
Be an encourager! When your friends become discouraged, be the one used by God to put the courage back into their lives. Exhort, support, back, promote, believe in, campaign for, be a spiritual fan that never misses a game and is always there to cheer from the sidelines. Encourage both by your life and by the Scriptures. Live with a contagious passion to help others see God more clearly and understand His ways more perfectly. The Greek word for exhort is *parakleet* (not parakeet) which literally means "to call alongside of" for help. Who (it could be many) has God called you to go alongside of to help and encourage in their walk with God? ____________________

____

Who is your exhorter? Who encourages you to be in God's Word and grow on a regular basis? ____________________
Jesus was a comforting exhorter to the diseased woman who touched His robe when He said, **Daughter, be of good comfort; your faith has made you whole** (Matthew 9:22). Jesus wants to comfort and encourage us! What did He ask Peter to write down for us in 1 Peter 5:7? ____________________

____

Encourage! Stay encouraged by God so you can be used of God to encourage others.

He that giveth, let him do it with simplicity
Be a giver! Give willingly. Give generously. Give liberally. Give to meet the needs of the needy. Be a giver. Give from the heart. Give without expecting anything in return. Give to others as God has given to you. The word **simplicity** reveals the simple purity of mind and sincerity of heart that is devoid of any ulterior motive. It explains the heart of the widow woman in Luke 21:1-5. Read this convicting passage and explain how her example could be a testimony (or even conviction) to you.

> **And He looked up, and saw the rich men casting their gifts into the treasury. And He saw also a certain poor widow casting in thither two mites. And He said, Of a truth I say unto you, that this poor widow hath cast in more than they all: for all these have of their abundance cast in unto the offerings of God: but she of her penury hath cast in all the living that she had.** Luke 21:1-4

____

____

Jesus certainly was gifted in giving. He gave the ultimate gift as stated in Galatians 1:4, **Who gave Himself for our sins, that He might deliver us from this present evil world, according to the will of God and our Father.** If God has given to you, give without expecting more, give without feelings of being used, give without a desire for recognition, give because you find joy and peace in giving. Through the years as I have traveled, I've bought presents for my wife and kids. Suppose I sent the gifts with a note, "I'm sending these gifts to you so that you will love me." They all would let me know that they loved me regardless of the gifts. Suppose I sent a note saying, "I'm sending these gifts to you because I love you!" Now they know why the gifts were given. In what ways do many struggle with the gift of giving?

____

He that ruleth, with diligence

Be a leader! Lead! Diligently take your leadership seriously. Know where you are going, how you are going to get there, and what you expect when you arrive. Be more than a good leader, be a great leader. Real men (real leaders) race toward the problems and try to fix them. In a way, we are all leaders. We are either drawing others closer to our Lord or driving them farther away. The concept of **diligence** (*spoude*) clarifies a true leader's approach to life. When you meditate on the words speed, urgency, hasten, earnestness, and zeal, you should get an idea of the personality of diligence. Diligence is an action word. Action is the enemy of apathy. How does diligence express the **heartily** of Colossians 3:23 and the **fervency** of Romans 12:11? ______________________________

____

Jesus was a leader. When He said "**Follow Me!**" (Matthew 16:24; Mark 10:21; Luke 9:23; John 12:26), He was giving an invitation for all to accept Him as the leader of their lives. In what ways do you follow Christ each day? ______________________________

____

He that showeth mercy, with cheerfulness

Be cheerful! Show kindness! Do it gladly, cheerfully, because you want to and not because you have to (no martyr's complex please). Be merciful to others because of the mercy that God has shown to you; do not be merciful so you can receive mercy from others. Mercy is motivated by pity. Pity for those with spiritual needs is not just feeling sorry for them, but a willingness to remove their miseries from them. Our Lord Jesus Christ removed our miseries by dying for us; we can help to remove the miseries of others by living for them. Who can you encourage (by removing a tear from their eyes and putting a smile on their hearts) today? ______________________________

How many have cried to our Lord, "**Have mercy on me!**" and received it? Most of us. So, if you cheerfully encourage others by sincerely giving of yourself and leading them closer to our merciful God, you are using your God-given gifts—just like Christ!

Be a merciful, cheerful encourager, giver, and leader—just like your Lord!

Sunday Review and Meditation

"Lord, thank You for saving me from my sin and delivering me from its consequences through Jesus Christ my Lord!"

Think! Think! Think!

Read Monday's study and explain how the principles of Romans 12:3 have impacted your life.

Accept who you are.

Read Tuesday's study and explain how the truths of Romans 12:4-5 have challenged your life.

Love one another.

Read Wednesday's study and explain how the teaching of Romans 12:4-5 has convicted you.

Thank God for His grace gifts!

Read Thursday's study and explain how the command of Romans 12:6-8 has altered your life.

Use your gifts for God!

Read Friday's study and explain how the confrontation of Romans 12:6-8 has made you think.

Encourage others, give to others, and lead others in a merciful way.

Read Saturday's study and explain how the exhortation of Romans 12:6-8 can change your life.

Monday: Romans 12

Practice genuine love.

Let love be without dissimulation. Abhor that which is evil; cleave to that which is good. Romans 12:9

Others have translated and paraphrased these thoughts and practical admonitions in expressions such as...

- Let love be without hypocrisy. Abhor what is evil. Cling to what is good.
- Let love be genuine. Abhor what is evil; hold fast to what is good.
- Love must be sincere. Hate what is evil; cling to what is good.
- Don't just pretend to love others. Really love them. Hate what is wrong. Hold tightly to what is good.
- Love from the center of who you are; don't fake it. Run for dear life from evil; hold on for dear life to good.

Let your love be real by sincerely hating the evil that could destroy the loved one's life and consistently clinging to the good that could encourage the loved one's heart. If someone questions if you are for real, they will see their answer in the way that you hate evil and cling to good. Don't just pretend that you love others, really love them.

Without dissimulation is another way of saying no hypocrisy. The Greek word *hupokrites* is the root from where we get our word hypocrisy. Today, teens and adults alike are looking for reality. There is way too much "faking it" in our relationship with God and others know when someone is genuine or not. Do others think you are real? Why or why not? Explain how God describes real love, real faith, and real wisdom.

Let your love be real! **Since you have purified your souls in obeying the truth through the Spirit in sincere love of the brethren, love one another fervently with a pure heart.** 1 Peter 1:22 ____________________

____

Let your faith be real! **When I call to remembrance the unfeigned faith that is in thee, which dwelt first in thy grandmother Lois, and thy mother Eunice; and I am persuaded that in thee also.** 2 Timothy 1:5 ____________________

____

Let your wisdom be real! **But the wisdom that is from above is first pure, then peaceable, gentle, and easy to be entreated, full of mercy and good fruits, without partiality, and without hypocrisy.** James 3:17____________________

____

Let love be without dissimulation. Abhor that which is evil; cleave to that which is good. Romans 12:9 ____________________

____

Before I can determine whether or not my love for others is genuine, I have to inspect my heart to see if my love for God is real. This can only be done through a slow read of Mark 12:30-31 which gives four aspects of sincere love and real commitment.

And thou shalt love the Lord thy God with all thy heart, and with all thy soul, and with all thy mind, and with all thy strength: this is the first commandment. And the second

is like, namely this, Thou shalt love thy neighbor as thyself. There is none other commandment greater than these.
Do I sincerely **love** God with all my **heart**? (Are there other lovers competing for first place in my heart? Am I intellectually and willfully determined to love my God?) ____________

____

Do I sincerely **love** God with all my **soul**? (This is the emotional part of our love as seen when Christ's soul was deeply grieved while at Gethsemane. Does my selfishness grieve my heart as much as it does my Lord's?) ____________

____

Do I sincerely **love** God with all my **mind**? (What I allow to consume and control my thoughts is what I truly care about! What I think about the most is what I love the most!)

____

____

Do I sincerely **love** God with all my **strength**? (Do I drain my energies for myself or my God? As age increases and strength decreases, can I look back without regrets on how I used my strength?) ____________

____

Abhor that which is evil: To honestly and sincerely love God like He loves me, I must hate sin! God reminds us in Psalm 97:10, **You who love the Lord, hate evil!** Do I utterly detest or view with horror that which displeases God? Do I seek to separate from such evil? What will be evident in a person's life who hates evil? ____________

____

____

Do you truly hate trivial sins as well as great sins? ____________
Do you sincerely hate secret sins as well as public sins? ____________

Cleave to that which is good: To honestly and sincerely love God like He loves me, I must view **good** in a 1 Thessalonians 5:15 way: **See that none render evil for evil unto any man; but ever follow that which is good.** It is easier to follow after **good** if you **cleave to** it. To **cleave** is to glue or cement yourself to. There are some glues that solvents can't touch. When we are superglued to good things, good people, or good works, solvents like peer pressure, public acceptance, and laziness cannot detach us from such good. What **good** have you spiritually superglued yourself to? ____________

____

____

____

Let love be without dissimulation. Abhor that which is evil; cleave to that which is good. Since this is the way I am to love God, do you think that God wants me to love others with the same unselfish love? ____________

____

____

____

____

Practice genuine love!

Tuesday: Romans 12

Love and honor others.

Be kindly affectioned one to another with brotherly love; in honor preferring one another. Romans 12:10

Most of us are born with a competitive nature. Most want to win and few love to lose. In a way, this simple verse of fourteen English words (only nine Greek words) is issuing a challenge to each of us to love each other with a brotherly affection (which sometimes is a challenge in itself) and then to "outdo one another" in showing such love and honor to each other. As we accept the challenge to engage in some friendly competition, what are the rules and how do you know if you win or lose?

Be kindly affectioned (with brotherly love) one to another

Love each other with the genuine affection that should be seen in family relationships. This **brotherly love** is so unique, God had to make up a word to explain it that is not found in ordinary Greek. Sad to say, selfishness has crawled into our homes in tsunami proportions and many brothers and sisters have never experienced the kind of love that Paul is talking about here. Even parents have learned to love self so much that they have lost the innate, natural love that even the animal kingdom expresses within its own families. On a scale of one to ten, how loving and kind are your family members to each other? What specific areas could use some change? ______________________________

____

It is almost as if God, through many writers of Scripture, assumes that all of us understand the loving, kind, quality relationships that we should have toward our family members. Explain what is "assumed" for families in the following verses.

Like as a father pitieth his children, so the Lord pitieth them that fear Him. Psalm 103:13______________________________

____

For whom the Lord loveth He correcteth; even as a father the son in whom he delighteth. Proverbs 3:12 ______________________________

____

But we were gentle among you, even as a nurse (young nursing mother) **cherisheth her children.** 1 Thessalonians 2:7 ______________________________

____

As ye know how we exhorted and comforted and charged every one of you, as a father doth his children. 1 Thessalonians 2:11 ______________________________

____

But as touching brotherly love ye need not that I write unto you: for ye yourselves are taught of God to love one another. 1 Thessalonians 4:9______________________________

____

Let brotherly love continue. Hebrews 13:1 ______________________________

____

How do you treat those in your family? Do you pity instead of attack; delight in rather than cut down; cherish rather than ignore; comfort rather than irritate; love rather than dislike? God assumes that we should love those we live with. Do you?________________________
If you hesitated on that answer, whose forgiveness do you need to seek and what needs to change right away? ____

____

In honor preferring one another

In our selfish world today, too few **love one another with brotherly love**. Someone needs to take the lead and set an example for others to follow! Always be a step ahead. Don't play the "Yeah, me too" game. Don't follow another in this but take the lead and be the example and pacesetter. It is almost like a contest seeing who can outdo the other in showing honor and giving preference. Now, the only way that we can honestly and genuinely esteem others above ourselves is twofold: refuse to judge their motives and keep a humble view of (judge) your own heart. We do not know what is in the hearts of others and hardly understand what motivates our own hearts.

Number One: Refuse to judge the motives of others.

1 Corinthians 2:11 asks, Who can know a person's thoughts except that person's own spirit? We cannot read minds and therefore have no right attacking those who disagree with us on preferential issues. Since we cannot read minds, what can we do to understand motives? ____
Before you attack others, <u>ask others</u>. Explain and apply the wise counsel found in Proverbs 1:5, **A wise man** (husband, wife, parent, child, friend) **will hear** (take time to listen)**, and will increase learning; and a man of understanding shall attain unto wise counsels.**

____

____

____

Number Two: Keep a humble view of your own heart.

How did the publican view his own heart in Luke 18:13? ______________________________

____

How did the Apostle Paul see himself in Romans 7:24? ______________________________

____

How did David describe his wandering from God in Psalm 119:176? __________________

____

An honest appraisal of the depravity of our own heart is essential to walking humbly with our God and prefering others above ourselves. It is not natural to put others first in our "me-first" world. Mr. and Mrs. Haughtypride (by putting on a good front) love the front seats, the front of lines, and the front pages. If given the perfect opportunity to sin with a promise of no one knowing and no consequences, what would you be capable of doing? __________

____

Remember, at the foot of the cross, we are all wicked, selfish sinners in need of forgiveness. All men are created equal in their depraved state.

Wednesday: Romans 12

Serve God with an enthusiastic, fervent attitude!

Not slothful in business; fervent in spirit; serving the Lord. Romans 12:11

There is really only one way to serve our wonderful Lord and thank Him for delivering us from our enslaving sin. Serve Him and others with a fervent, zealous, outrageous, contagious enthusiasm! Serve out of love and you will love to serve. Combine a fervent inward attitude with a diligent, outward action, and you will have a true, biblical, fervent servant of God. Actually, Romans 12:10-12 gives a list of ten ways to serve others and verse 11 gives numbers three, four, and five in that list of ten.

Not slothful in business

Don't be lazy. Never be lacking in zeal. Enjoy working hard. Work in such a way that you get tired on purpose. If laziness was a poison, diligence would be its antidote. If apathy was a disease, fervency would be its cure. If indifference was a math problem, enthusiastic intensity would be its solution. Describe what frustrations you would face if you were assigned the job of cleaning a junior high school every night for one year and had two lazy, indifferent, apathetic coworkers. ____________________

____

____

The phrase **not slothful in business** is interesting to dissect. The word **slothful** (*okneros*) means to be slow, to delay, to be tardy, or to be late. Synonyms such as heavy, burdensome, tiresome, slow, sluggish, and inactive help to describe the word's intent. The word **business** (*spoude*) has basically the very opposite meaning. It means to speed, to hasten, to hurry up, to earnestly and zealously attack a project or a problem. In a way, the entire phrase is saying, "Don't slow down your speed." Someone addicted to apathy would slothfully, lazily, lag behind those who earnestly, fervently, and zealously attack life's challenges. Is there anything that constantly and consistently slows you down in your service for God? If so, what is it and how can you deal with it in a strong biblical way? ____________________

____

____

Diligence does not understand laziness. If diligence is looking at each opportunity in life as a special assignment from the Lord and using every ounce of energy to accomplish it, how would you define laziness? ____________________

____

____

How would a lazy person argue against Colossians 3:23...**whatsoever ye do, do it heartily, as to the Lord** or Ecclesiastes 9:10...**whatsoever thy hand findeth to do, do it with thy might**? ____________________

____

Laziness is in essence a lack of whatever it takes to work hard, to work fast, and to work long. So, when we give in to laziness, what are we missing or lacking in life? ____________________
How would a lack of restful sleep affect laziness? ____________________

____

How would a lack of exercise and stamina influence laziness? ______________________

____

How would a lack of commitment impact laziness? ______________________

____

How would a lack of spiritual desire to please God affect laziness? ______________

____

Fervent in spirit

Someone has said that 80% of life is attitude. Our attitude or **spirit** in life is long remembered after what we say is forgotten. Paul is encouraging us to be **fervent in spirit** which would convey a seething, scalding, boiling hot attitude toward serving Christ. Being **fervent in spirit** implies that this zeal has to come from the heart! It cannot be a fake, frothing at the mouth, emotional pretence, but real heart fervency. Keep your spiritual fervor. Simply care enough to let it grab hold of your heart in such a way you are totally committed and enthusiastically involved. How do you keep such fervency of heart day after day? The answer is hidden in the Heidelberg Catechism and what this six-week study is all about. Remember, we ruined our lives in sin; God's remedy is Jesus Christ; so how can we live our lives in a way that thanks God for what He has done for us? How will a faith-filled visit to the cross keep you fervent, hot, and intensely committed to serving your Lord?

____

____

____

Serving the Lord

How can serving be spiritually, emotionally, and physically draining? (Acts 20:19 **Serving the Lord with all humility of mind, and with many tears, and temptations.**) __________

____

How does serving involve "all" your heart and soul? (Deuteronomy 10:12-13...**what doth the Lord thy God require of thee...to serve the Lord thy God with all thy heart and with all thy soul**...) ____

____

____

____

How is serving a choice? (Joshua 24:15 **And if it seem evil unto you to serve the Lord, choose you this day whom ye will serve...but as for me and my house, we will serve the Lord.**) ____

____

____

____

How does serving involve a wholesome dread of apathetic serving and an overwhelming awe of the Lord Whom we have the privilege to serve? (Psalm 2:11 **Serve the Lord with fear, and rejoice with trembling.**) ______________________________

____

"Lord, help me to be not slothful in business; fervent in spirit;
serving You, Lord."

Thursday: Romans 12

Patiently rejoice and continually pray.

Rejoicing in hope; patient in tribulation; continuing instant in prayer.
Romans 12:12

With a merry and joyful heart motivated by what will be in the future, don't give in to what has been in the past and don't give up to what is presently troubling you today. Be devoted to prayer—thanking God for what He has allowed in the past and trusting God for what He is permitting in the present and providing for the future.

Rejoicing in hope
Chairo is the Greek word for **rejoicing**, gladness, or joy. The "Chairo Attitude" is the best way to pick up the heavy burdens of life and successfully carry them to the end of life. **Is any among you afflicted? Let him pray. Is any merry? Let him sing psalms** (James 5:13). Biblical hope is not the hope of a "I hope I make it" or a "I hope so" lifestyle, but the happy anticipation and joyful eagerness of experiencing firsthand what our Lord has in store for us. We know that He is preparing a place for us (John 14:1-3) and that no one can even imagine the things which God is preparing for those who love Him (1 Corinthians 2:9). How can the **hope** of what God is preparing for us empower and encourage us as we face difficulties and trials today? ______________________________

____

____

____

Patient (persevering) in tribulation
Those who possess patient endurance can persevere under a heavy load without complaining, griping, or giving up. It would be like picking up a loaded backpack full of miseries, adversities, persecutions, and difficulties and carrying it with the strength supplied by a sustaining God. If you had to make a checklist of the heavy load in your personal backpack, what difficulties and trials would be on your list? ______________

____

____

____

____

____

One of the most encouraging passages of Scripture I have ever studied is found at the end of 2 Corinthians 4. **For which cause we faint not; but though our outward man perish, yet the inward man is renewed day by day. For our light affliction, which is but for a moment, worketh for us a far more exceeding and eternal weight of glory; while we look not at the things which are seen, but at the things which are not seen: for the things which are seen are temporal; but the things which are not seen are eternal** (2 Corinthians 4:16-18). Here God is encouraging us to not lose heart because our present troubles won't last very long. If we can take our focus off our temporary troubles and focus on the eternal, glorious experiences that God has for us, we can persevere and not give up no matter how great the affliction.

Explain how 2 Corinthians 4:16-18 helps us to be **rejoicing in hope** and **patient in tribulation.** ____

(When you have time, meditate on the truths which deal with endurance, patient endurance, and joyful perseverance found in Matthew 10:22, 24:13; Mark 13:13; 2 Timothy 2:10,12; Hebrews 10:32; James 1:12, 5:11; and 1 Peter 2:20.)

Continuing instant in prayer

Interestingly enough, to endure you must endure. To patiently endure under trials and troubles you must steadfastly and faithfully endure in prayer. What is the difference between being devoted to prayer and dabbling in prayer? ____

The Complete Word Study Dictionary edited by Spiros Zodhiates states that the original word for continuing instant (*proskartereo*) means to tarry, remain somewhere (Mark 3:9); to continue steadfastly with someone (Acts 8:13); to cleave faithfully to someone (Acts 10:7); referring to those who continually insist on something or stay close to someone (Romans 13:6).[16] Referring to the verses listed below, and using the words tarry, remain, continue steadfastly, and cleave faithfully, paint a word picture of someone who is totally devoted to God by being devoted to both His Word and prayer.

Men ought always to pray, and not to faint. Luke 18:1
Praying always with all prayer and supplication in the Spirit, and watching thereunto with all perseverance and supplication for all saints. Ephesians 6:18
Continue in prayer, and watch in the same with thanksgiving. Colossians 4:2
Pray without ceasing. 1 Thessalonians 5:17

____

Do you rejoice in hope? ____
Are you patient in tribulation? ____
Do you continue instant in prayer? ____

If you do, not only is God being pleased, and not only are you growing in grace, but you are demonstrating to God your thankful heart for His forgiveness and redemptive plan for your life. We can all say "amen" to such a joy.

Friday: Romans 12

Give as God has given to you!

Distributing to the necessity of saints; given to hospitality. Romans 12:13

Paul encouraged Timothy to encourage the "haves" to help the "have-nots" by being willing to give. **Charge them that are rich in this world, that they be not highminded, nor trust in uncertain riches, but in the living God, who giveth us richly all things to enjoy; that they do good, that they be rich in good works, ready to distribute, willing to communicate** (1 Timothy 6:17-18). No one enjoys asking for money from others. Today, Paul could be a modern-day CFO. His understanding of both the complicated financial pictures and economic pressures put on those who have dedicated their lives to serving Christ and His gospel is exceptional. Those who are rich are not to be proud or trust in their unreliable money (which could disappear by tomorrow). The rich are to trust God who gave them all that they have for their enjoyment in the first place. The rich should use their money for good, be generous to those in need, and always being ready to share with others. Describe the giving part of your worship to God. Do you tithe? Do you only tithe or do you give offerings also? What percentage of your income do you give back to God? If you were to counsel a young couple on how they should honor God with their giving, explain your counsel and give two Scripture references that back up your advice to them.

____

____

____

____

Distributing to the necessity of saints

- Share with God's people who are in need.
- Share what you have been given to those in need.
- Does God possibly want to supply the needs of His saints through you?

You cannot share *with* a person without sharing *in* a person's life. When you become a partner you are "part of" that individual and his ministry. True sharing is never one-sided. There is an established partnership and an understood mutual sharing. One may share the bucks and the other may share the blessings, but both are overjoyed by being used by God. Write down some blessing from your past that was a direct result of your willingness to share financially with a ministry in need. ______________________________

____

____

____

Now, we have to do our study and learn to discern a "real need" from a "created crisis" before we ever give. Make sure your giving will be used for its intended purpose and the gospel message will be heard because of your generosity.

The Bible has much to say about giving. Read each principle and passage and comment on how Scripture should be the solid foundation for why and how we give.

1. Giving should be kept a secret between us and God. (Matthew 6:1-4) ______________

____

2. Our giving should be motivated by love and compassion. (1 John 3:17) ______________

____

3. We must give cheerfully (because we want to) and not grudgingly (because we have to). (Romans 12:8; 2 Corinthians 9:7) ____

____

4. Save in order to give. Always be ready when a true need arises. (Proverbs 3:27-28) _____

____

5. Give out of thanksgiving for what God has given to you. (1 Chronicles 29:13-14)

____

6. Give out of honor to God: not out of the surplus at the end of the month, but out of the abundance of the day after the paycheck is deposited. (Proverbs 3:9-10) ______________

____

7. Remember God's promise to those who give, but never allow the happiness of getting take precedence over the joy of giving. (Luke 6:38) ________________________________

____

Given to hospitality

- Driven with dogged determination (**given**), show kindness to strangers (**hospitality**).
- Be eager to practice hospitality, desiring to open your home to whoever is in need.
- Be willing to give of your comforts, your space, and your personal zone to help those who are away from their own comforts, space, and personal zones.
- Don't just show hospitality when you are asked to, but eagerly go out of your way to offer it to others. Let your heart be the host for those who are hurting. How do you fulfill this command on a regular basis? ____

____

____

____

Showing **hospitality** does have its trials and inconveniences. Benjamin Franklin said, "Fish and company stink after three days." Being hospitable to those who become fishlike is not always easy. Some friends, because of their short stay, keep unreasonable hours and rob the host family from the much needed rest. Others are snackaholics who come, empty the pantries, and move on to the snack cupboards of other unsuspecting friends. Some back up their tractor trailers of troubles to your front door, dump a truckload of sorrows on your family, and then leave! When you compare your initial response (what you want to say or do) with your godly heart's response (what you should say or do), you see how much growth you need in the art of **hospitality**. Remember what both Peter and his friend who wrote Hebrews remind us: **use hospitality one to another without grudging**, and, **be not forgetful to entertain strangers: for thereby some have entertained angels unawares** (1 Peter 4:9 and Hebrews 13:2). Have you had any angels over for supper lately?

Give as God has given you!

Saturday: Romans 12

Ask God to bless those who persecute you.

Bless them which persecute you: bless, and curse not. Romans 12:14

Here God gives another short verse that is to the point, easily understood, and sad to say, often disregarded or defiantly disobeyed. There are only three words in this verse that have the possibility of being misunderstood: **bless**, **persecute**, and **curse**.

Bless them

The word **bless** comes from two Greek words: (*eulogéœ*) *eú*—good or well, and *lógos*—word. Together they mean to speak well of. It is not merely saying nice things about those who curse you or curse your God, but it is asking God to give His blessing upon them by doing His work of salvation and sanctification in their lives. If your enemies or persecutors knew Jesus Christ as their personal Savior or were walking with God, do you think they would be acting the same way toward you? Think of someone you have a difficult time with; got them in your mind? Now, look at them as they "would" be if they knew God and were walking close to God. In a few short words, describe the transformation of that person that just took place in your mind. ______________________________

____

____

____

The concept of the word **bless** has been trivialized and cheapened to the point of it becoming simply a nice cliché. When someone sneezes some say, "God bless you," and many who do not even know God sing "God Bless America." In the South, the phrase "Bless your heart" is a nice way to say whatever you want about someone and still come across caring and kind. "Why he's as ugly as a bullfrog, bless his heart." "She's got the personality of a doorknob, bless her heart." There are times when we can do or say something that becomes a real "blessing" to others. A $20 bill, a thank-you note, a cup of coffee, taking the time to go and pray for someone who is struggling, babysitting so a busy couple can go out on a date, washing someone's car, sharing the gospel, buying a bag of groceries, and the list goes on and on. In fact, list ten more ways to be a blessing to those around you.

____

____

____

____

____

Be a blessing. If you need to bless those who persecute you, wouldn't you assume that you would bless those who irritate you, provoke you, exasperate you, or ignore you? Is there anyone in your life, right now, that exasperates you? Rattles your cage? Drives you up a wall? Hounds you? Drives you to an insane asylum? How well is your "blesser" working?

____

Which persecute you

Do you ever feel persecuted, discriminated against, or bullied? People can be mean. Bullies are fearful people who attack those who are different. When I say "different," it could be a different race, a different religion, or a different political position. It could also mean a difference in the way they dress, look, think, walk, or live. It is sad that there are those in our world who ridicule and make fun of anyone or anything that is different. Describe how someone at your school or your work gets "persecuted" on a daily basis just because they are a little bit different.____

____

____

The ridicule and mocking that we face today cannot even be compared with the persecution that Roman Christians experienced. They were abused. They were beaten. They were tortured. They were killed. In our world, we can hardly imagine that. Explain how the following two passages encouraged the hearts of both the persecuted Christians in Rome and the ridiculed Christians in your life.

> **Blessed are they which are persecuted for righteousness' sake: for theirs is the kingdom of heaven. Blessed are ye, when men shall revile you, and persecute you, and shall say all manner of evil against you falsely, for My sake. Rejoice, and be exceeding glad: for great is your reward in heaven: for so persecuted they the prophets which were before you.** Matthew 5:10-12

> **Blessed are ye, when men shall hate you, and when they shall separate you from their company, and shall reproach you, and cast out your name as evil, for the Son of man's sake. Rejoice ye in that day, and leap for joy: for, behold, your reward is great in heaven: for in the like manner did their fathers unto the prophets.** Luke 6:22-23

____

____

____

____

Bless, and curse not

Just as the word **bless** means to call for God's favor to be poured out on an individual, so the word **curse** means to call for God's judgment to be poured out. Anyone who screams in anger for God to damn a person, does not really know what they is saying. If they experienced five seconds in hell, they would never ask God to do so. The main reason we should **bless and curse not**, is that your persecutor may be to you what Saul was to Stephen. At the trial of Sir Thomas More, after being sentenced to death, his last words were, "My lords, I have but to say that, like as the blessed apostle St. Paul was present at the death of the martyr Stephen, keeping their clothes that stoned him, and yet be now both saints in heaven, and there shall continue friends for ever, so I trust, and shall therefore pray, that though your lordships have been on earth my judges, yet we may hereafter meet in heaven together, to our everlasting salvation."[17] How can you apply this man's words and Luke's words in Luke 6:27-28 to your life today?___________________________________

____

____

____

But I say unto you which hear, Love your enemies, do good to them which hate you, bless them that curse you, and pray for them which despitefully use you. Matthew 5:44

Sunday Review and Meditation

"Lord, thank You for saving me from my sin and delivering me from its consequences through Jesus Christ my Lord!"

Practice genuine love.

Read Monday's study and explain how the principles of Romans 12:9 have impacted your life.

____
____
____
____
____
____

Love and honor others.

Read Tuesday's study and explain how the truths of Romans 12:10 have challenged your life.

____
____
____
____
____
____

Serve God with an enthusiastic, fervent attitude!

Read Wednesday's study and explain how the teaching of Romans 12:11 has convicted you.

____
____
____
____
____
____

Patiently rejoice and continually pray.

Read Thursday's study and explain how the command of Romans 12:12 has altered your life.

Give as God has given to you!

Read Friday's study and explain how the confrontation of Romans 12:13 has made you think.

Ask God to bless those who persecute you.

Read Saturday's study and explain how the exhortation of Romans 12:14 can change your life.

Monday: Romans 12

Love others so much that you can rejoice and weep with them.

Rejoice with them that do rejoice, and weep with them that weep. Romans 12:15

In some ways, Paul repeats himself (by inspiration, of course). How would the following Romans 12 principles overlap with Paul's rejoice-rejoice/weep-weep principle?

Let love be unhypocritical (9) ______________________________

____

Kindly affectionate one to another (10) ______________________________

____

In honor preferring one another (10) ______________________________

____

Rejoicing in hope (12) ______________________________

____

Bless and don't curse (14)______________________________

____

What would hinder this simple command? Why would anyone "not" want to rejoice with someone who is rejoicing? Here are some thoughts. Write your comments.

Selfish focus: "No one rejoices with me!"______________________________

____

Envy and jealousy: "Why do they get all the good stuff?"______________________________

____

Critical and judgmental: "They probably stole it or begged for it!" ______________________________

____

Self absorbed: "Why does God love them more than He does me?" ______________________________

____

It always seems easier to **weep with them that weep** than to **rejoice with them that rejoice**. Why? Because it is not difficult to hurt for those who are experiencing something you hope and pray will never happen in your own life. But it is difficult to be happy and rejoice with someone who is blessed by God in a way that you have wanted to be blessed for years (and fear that you never will)! Think about it. Is it easier to console a friend who lost a job or congratulate a friend who was just hired (for the job that you applied for)? Is it easier to comfort a friend who just broke off an engagement or rejoice with a friend who just got married (to a person you dated in the past)? Our prayer needs to be, "Lord, teach me to be enthusiastically happy in my heart for others when You bless them in a way that I have been praying that You would bless me." How do you personally struggle with rejoicing with those who rejoice?______________________________

____

Weep with them that weep

How do people know when someone really cares? How do "we" know if we really care? In the day of Christ, professional mourners would come for the sad event, cry, mourn, and move on. Fake mourners who tore their clothes made sure they tore them on a seam so they could easily sew them up for future mourning opportunities. True "weeping with weepers" consists of a continued interest that seeks to help the afflicted through their many levels of grief. The Lord "wept" for Mary and Martha because of the loss of Lazarus, but then He (as God, of course) did something about relieving their grief. Paul is not asking for us to "fake it" as hired mourners, but to sincerely and honestly seek to feel others' pain and hurt with them. You cannot manufacture tears on command. Tear ducts have their reservoir in the heart and can only flow when the heart is squeezed. Describe the last time you had the opportunity to weep with someone who was really hurting. ______________

____

____

How can the following Bible principles help you to truly care from your heart and not just react out of duty, guilt, or the expectations of others?

Those believers who are hurting are part of your spiritual family. Romans 12:5 __________

____

God trusts those who are hurting in the midst of a crisis, difficulty, or tragedy to depend on Him for the grace to endure through it. James 2:1-4 ______________________

____

You may be next! How do you want others to comfort you when cancer, death, trials, or tragedies enter into your heart or home? Galatians 6:1 ______________________

____

As part of the loving family of God, you know that those hurting cannot expect sympathy from a cold and unfeeling world. 1 Peter 1:22 ______________________

____

Who has ever been envious of trials, heartaches, and rejection? How does it comfort your heart when others cry with you? **Now when Job's three friends heard of all this evil that was come upon him, they came every one from his own place; Eliphaz the Temanite, and Bildad the Shuhite, and Zophar the Naamathite: for they had made an appointment together to come to mourn with him and to comfort him.** Job 2:11

____

Why is it sad that there are so few "weeping prophets" left? **Oh that my head were waters, and mine eyes a fountain of tears, that I might weep day and night for the slain of the daughter of my people.** Jeremiah 9:1 ______________________

____

Why should we think about how others feel before we focus on how we feel? **Remember them that are in bonds, as bound with them; and them which suffer adversity, as being yourselves also in the body.** Hebrews 13:3 ______________________

____

Simply love others enough to truly rejoice with them that rejoice and genuinely weep with them that weep. God can give you the grace to love others in this way. He can!

Tuesday: Romans 12

Humbly enjoy the company of all of God's family.

Be of the same mind one toward another. Mind not high things, but condescend to men of low estate. Be not wise in your own conceits. Romans 12:16

How can I show my thankfulness to God for saving me from my terrible sin? In one word, humility. In one sentence, live in harmony with others and don't be so proud, haughty, or conceited that you can't enjoy hanging out with ordinary people! Pride scares me. I know that I cannot live a godly, consistent Christian life without the grace of God. I also know that the only thing that would keep me from God's grace is my own stinking pride. God resists the proud and only gives grace to the humble. My treatment of others (even those that others would look down on) reveals my heart.

Be of the same mind one toward another.
Lovingly decide and unselfishly choose to think harmoniously with others in your life (which includes those you work with, those you go to school with, and those you live at home with). To do this...

...you'll need to carefully consider their thoughts.
...you'll need to understand them and know them well.
...you'll need to refuse to deceive yourself that they have it out for you.
...you'll need to realize that you cannot judge anyone's heart or motives.
...you'll need to know that just because you disagree with someone does not insist that either one of you are wrong, but that you each look at life from your own context, giftedness, and background.

Without listing any names, describe a situation that you are currently struggling through and need to apply some of the principles above to gain victory in your soul. ____________

____

____

____

Explain how the following passages both confront and comfort your heart as you journey through life seeking the humility to keep the right view of other believers.

- **Now the God of patience and consolation grant you to be likeminded one toward another according to Christ Jesus: that ye may with one mind and one mouth glorify God, even the Father of our Lord Jesus Christ.** Romans 15:5-6
- **Fulfil ye my joy, that ye be likeminded, having the same love, being of one accord, of one mind. Let nothing be done through strife or vainglory; but in lowliness of mind let each esteem other better than themselves.** Philippians 2:2-3
- **Finally, be ye all of one mind, having compassion one of another, love as brethren, be pitiful, be courteous.** 1 Peter 3:8

____

____

____

____

Mind not high things, but condescend to men of low estate.
If Paul were writing today, it might sound something like this: "Don't be a proud, haughty, know-it-all! Be willing to hang out with us lowly, ordinary people who may not be rich, good-looking, or popular, but may have much more to offer than you think. Don't think

you are everything and others are nothing! Cultivate humility by letting the lowly lead your thinking." How can pride impact a leader's influence on those he is leading? ___________

____

The words, **mind not**, are not a suggestion to consider, but a command to obey. Maybe you've heard a parent or a teacher say something like, "Mind you now!" or "You kids better mind!" which is a nice way of saying, "Think!" Now, this command tells us what not to think about. Stop thinking about yourself! Refuse to believe that you are some wonderful, great gift to mankind and that your work, school, or church probably would not be what it is without you. Don't be proud! What does Proverbs 13:10 say about a proud, haughty, overbearing view of self? **Only by pride cometh contention: but with the well advised is wisdom.** ____

____

Normally we would hear a mom say, "Alright now, don't get carried away!" But in this case, God is saying, "Alright now, let's get carried away with lowly people and lowly tasks." What is lowly or insignificant in man's eyes may not be so lowly in God's eyes. Whether I preach to 150 or 1,500 I should be "carried away" with the needs of either group. The 150 may seem lowly to those dealing with 1,500; the 1,500 is lowly to those filling stadiums with 15,000. Be careful who you consider lowly. Who was considered lowly in 2 Corinthians 10:1? _____

____

Who else did God use the word lowly (*tapeinos*) to describe in Matthew 11:28-30? _______

____

Be not wise in your own conceits.

Never be conceited. Do not create the habit of becoming a know-it-all! Don't be full of yourself! Don't be blinded in your own eyes to who and what you really are before God (and before men). Those full of themselves have little room for others. The first point in the Heidelberg Catechism (which we meditated on the first week of this study) reminds us that we have ruined our lives in sin. The best antidote for a conceited, proud heart is a return visit to the cross. Before Calvary we are all sinners. Sinners are sinners. If you are intelligent, rich, physically fit, and very successful, then you are an intelligent sinner, a wealthy sinner, a physically attractive sinner, and a prosperous, successful sinner...but still a sinner. Pride concerns God! What is God trying to teach us and warn us about in the following verses?

Seest thou a man wise in his own conceit? There is more hope of a fool than of him. Proverbs 26:12 ____

____

And if any man think that he knoweth anything, he knoweth nothing yet as he ought to know. But if any man love God, the same is known of him. 1 Corinthians 8:2-3

____

Be of the same mind one toward another. Mind not high things, but condescend to men of low estate. Be not wise in your own conceits. Romans 12:16

Wednesday: Romans 12

Respect others and refuse to retaliate for any reason.

Recompense to no man evil for evil. Provide things honest in the sight of all men. Romans 12:17

Recompense

Refuse to pay back evil for evil to anyone. Respect what is right in the sight of all men by seriously thinking about what is honorable, right, and best in the eyes of everybody involved. In areas of revenge, retaliation, or expressions of bitterness, we are not to be debtors in any way. Is there anyone on earth that you wish you could make hurt as much as they have made you (or someone you love) hurt? How do you deal with those who have hurt or offended you in the past? ______________________________

____

____

How does true, biblical forgiveness free you from such a desire to retaliate? ______________

____

____

To no man

The "no way" phrase craze ("No way! Yes way!") has been around for some time. The Greek word (*medeis*) means none, not any, no one, in no way, not even one. We are not obligated, or even encouraged, to play "gotcha-last" with words or actions towards others. But what about the guy who stole my iPod? **To no man.** But what about the girl who lied about me on Facebook? **To no man.** But what about my dad for what he did...and my mom for allowing it? **To no man.** "You're it, I quit!" does not make it in our grown-up, mature world. (Or does it?) **No man:** regardless of what was said. **No man:** regardless of what was done. **No man:** regardless of how much it hurt. If anyone had the right to retaliate, it would have been our Lord Jesus Christ. Slowly read through the passage below and explain how Christ responded to those who hurt Him.

> **For even hereunto were ye called: because Christ also suffered for us, leaving us an example, that ye should follow His steps: who did no sin, neither was guile found in His mouth: who, when He was reviled, reviled not again; when He suffered, He threatened not; but committed Himself to Him that judgeth righteously.** 1 Peter 2:21-23

____

____

____

Evil for evil

Even though you have been the recipient of evil (bad, worthless, harmful, hurtful words, actions, or attitudes) you will never win by throwing the same back in their face. Someone has to stop! That someone is usually the one who allows God's grace to do a work in his or her heart. It is the someone who is open to God replacing an unforgiving heart with a forgiving, patient, broken heart. Giving back **evil for evil** results in an evil cycle that cannot stop unless someone refuses to retaliate.

- Only by pride comes contention—someone must stop!
- A soft answer turns away wrath—someone must stop!
- See that none render evil for evil—someone must stop!
- Recompense to no man evil for evil—someone must stop!

How do you stop? What is the key to ending such a vicious cycle? How would you counsel a friend who needed to stop retaliating? ____________________

____

____

____

What is God's answer? The key to stopping (putting off) anything is to renew your mind (putting in) and start starting (putting on). Check out Ephesians 4:22-24.

Provide things honest in the sight of all men

Again, our study today focuses on refusing to pay back evil for evil to anyone. Respect what is right in the sight of all men by seriously thinking about what is honorable, right, and best in the eyes of everybody involved. What mental process do you go through when you totally disagree with someone? How do you talk to them or about them? ____________

____

____

____

The word **provide** (*pronoéœ*) comes from two words: (*pro*) before and (*noéœ*) to think. In other words, we knew you were coming, and we are ready for you. We have not reacted but through honest contemplation, have acted accordingly. We have crawled into your shoes and attempted to see your side of the issue and understand why you think the way that you do. We want our attitudes and actions to be honorable, good, respectable, upright, admirable, worthy, principled, right. So, even if we disagree with others, after spending serious mental energy looking through their eyes, we will have the calmness of spirit and confidence of our own view so that no one will respond in ugly, unkind, or mean-spirited words.

In the sight of all men

Interestingly, we have a "no way" starting this verse and a "yes way" ending it: **to no man; to all men. No man** should ever experience an evil word, a hurtful action, or a wicked attitude from any of us; **all men** should experience kind words, considerate actions, and honorable, loving attitudes from all of us. Even though we are to **recompense to no man evil for evil**, we should be attune to repaying those who have impacted our lives in a positive way (parents, teachers, friends, pastors). Who needs a thank-you note or a love note from you today? ____________________

____

____

Obviously we are debtors to Christ and all He has sacrificed, paid, and given to us.
We can never pay back that debt.
Live your life in thanksgiving to God for His mercy.

Thursday: Romans 12

Live peaceably with all men (if it is possible).

If it be possible, as much as lieth in you, live peaceably with all men. Romans 12:18

No one can accuse Paul of being unbalanced. Living at peace with all men is not an easy task in a self-centered, self-focused, self-idolizing world. The phrase **as much as lieth in you** (so far as it depends on you) does put the responsibility on the mature Christian's shoulders. We need to do all we can! Your goal should be peace and not conflict. Your motivation should be nothing more than glorifying God by approaching others with a humble, loving, unselfish heart. So, is this possible for you?

If it be possible

If, if in any way, reaching deeply inside of yourself as far as you possibly can, if you are able, if you are capable, if there is any way...live peaceably with all men. This phrase is both subjective and hypothetical. Paul is saying, "I am not saying that you can; I am not saying that others will ever allow it to happen; I am not saying that it is even possible to do so; but, as much as it depends on you, live peaceably with all men." What do you do when you are asked to do the impossible? ____

____

____

Whenever I am asked to do the impossible my mind races to three Bible principles that give us the biblical foundation for the phrase, "I can't, but God can!"

...for without Me [Jesus] **ye can do nothing.** John 15:5
I can do all things through Christ who strengtheneth me. Philippians 4:13
With men this is impossible; but with God all things are possible. Matthew 19:26

Interesting enough, the root word for **it be possible** is *dunamai* which means to be able, strong, and powerful...dynamite powerful. Since we cannot generate such power within ourselves, where does this *dunamai* come from? Following each verse below, explain what God says about the power and divine enablement He offers us.

Finally, my brethren, be strong in the Lord, and in the power of His might. Ephesians 6:10 ____

____

That He would grant you, according to the riches of His glory, to be strengthened with might by His Spirit in the inner man. Ephesians 3:16 ______________________________

____

Strengthened with all might, according to His glorious power, unto all patience and longsuffering with joyfulness. Colossians 1:11 ______________________________

____

Thou therefore, my son, be strong in the grace that is in Christ Jesus. 2 Timothy 2:1

____

____

As much as lieth in you

Literally, out of you! Dig into your heart of hearts and look for the grace, love, and patience that God put there. This peaceable living must come "out of you" and not out of anyone else. You are the one that must use the soft answer; you are the one that must drop the pride; you are the one that must stop pushing the issue. Out of you! The peace, if it is possible at all, depends on you. You must do your part and try. Have you done (and are you doing) all that you can to be at peace with everyone you know? ____________________

Live peaceably with all men

Using the list of synonyms and antonyms below, write a short paragraph explaining what it means to **live peaceably with all men**. ____________________

____

____

____

Synonyms: concord, harmony, calmness, tranquility, serenity, freedom from strife, end of war, reconciled, and forgiven
Antonyms: to disturb, to agitate greatly, to make an uproar, to stir up, to arouse, to seek revenge, to fight, to declare war, conflict, hostility, and chaos

When we esteem others highly, prefer others before ourselves, seek to edify each other, and allow God's peace to rule in our hearts, we have such a greater chance to **live peaceably with all men**. Don't hold a grudge; never refuse forgiveness; release offenses to God; seek to understand why others think the way they do; think no evil; consider what it would be like if all were controlled by God's Spirit and unselfishly living for God; then you can live peaceably with all men. What does God promise to those who seek peace? **Finally, brethren, farewell. Be perfect, be of good comfort, be of one mind, live in peace; and the God of love and peace shall be with you.** 2 Corinthians 13:11 ____________________

____

____

____

How should those who seek peace view others? **And to esteem them very highly in love for their work's sake. And be at peace among yourselves.** 1 Thessalonians 5:13 ________

____

____

____

What should we follow after or look for in others? **Let us therefore follow after the things which make for peace, and things wherewith one may edify another.** Romans 14:19

____

____

____

And let the peace of God rule in your hearts. Colossians 3:15

Friday: Romans 12

Forgive. Don't retaliate. Let God do His just work.

Dearly beloved, avenge not yourselves, but rather give place unto wrath: for it is written, Vengeance is mine; I will repay, saith the Lord. Therefore if thine enemy hunger, feed him; if he thirst, give him drink: for in so doing thou shalt heap coals of fire on his head. Romans 12:19-20

Dear friends, never take revenge on others, but leave room for God to display His righteous anger. God wrote in His Word for all of us to read and to remember, "Vengeance is mine: I will take revenge, I will pay back those who have earned such vengeance! I will display My wrath in My way and My time."

Dearly beloved

This is the first time in the New Testament that Paul uses the phrase, **dearly beloved**. These two words are rooted in *agape* which denotes an unselfish love and concern for others rather than self. Each time Paul uses these words, he is getting ready to lay on them a firm confrontation, rebuke, warning, or command. Match the following.

- Dearly beloved, never take revenge ______________________________
- Dearly beloved, flee and run from idolatry ______________________________
- Dearly beloved, cleanse yourself from filthiness______________________________
- Dearly beloved, I beg you to get right with each other ______________________________
- Dearly beloved, I fear you're in sin and won't repent ______________________________
- Dearly beloved, don't fear or be ashamed ______________________________

Romans 12:19 • 1 Corinthians 10:14 • 2 Corinthians 7:1
2 Corinthians 12:19 • Philippians 4:1 • 2 Timothy 1:2

Beloved, dearly loved, my dear friends, my beloved friends, I am on your side! I am your friend! What I am about to tell you is not because I am upset, hateful, or looking for ways to make you miserable, I am going to love you enough to give you the truth and give it straight. Ready?

Avenge not yourselves, but rather give place unto wrath

Forgiveness is woven all through Romans 12:19-20. At the end of our first week and the beginning of our second week of study we read these words:

> As a sinner, I need forgiveness. Forgiveness is a promise (not a feeling) that my sin has been covered, dealt with, forgiven, so that it will not be brought up against me ever again. When God forgives, He justifies me. When God forgives, He declares me righteous. When God forgives He frees me from the guilt and penalty of my sin.

Is there anyone on earth (in your everyday life) that you refuse to forgive? ______________
Why is it so hard to forgive and let go of your vengeful feelings toward someone who hurt or offended you? ____

____

Remember, we are to forgive others in the same way that God has forgiven us (Ephesians 4:32). Forgiveness is not a feeling, but a promise. Forgiveness is not only a promise that we will not bring that sin up again, it is a release. We must release (let go of) our vengeful feelings toward those who sinned against us. Instead of us trying to be the judge and the jury, we must let go of the situation (and the individual) and trust God to deal with them in His way and His time. Don't retaliate. Don't attempt to hurt others as much as they hurt you. Get out of the way and let God deal with it.

For it is written, Vengeance is mine; I will repay, saith the Lord.
Just as God promises to forgive, He promises to judge sin. God is not only our loving Father but also our fearful Judge. Nahum, one of the minor prophets, reminds us that **God is jealous, and the Lord revengeth; the Lord revengeth, and is furious; the Lord will take vengeance on His adversaries, and He reserveth wrath for His enemies. The Lord is slow to anger, and great in power, and will not at all acquit the wicked** [clear the guilty] (Nahum 1:2-3). What could you do to punish someone you want to get back at? ________

____

How can God do a better job than us in passing judgment and choosing the just and proper punishment for the offender? ________________________________

____

Therefore if thine enemy hunger, feed him; if he thirst, give him drink: for in so doing thou shalt heap coals of fire on his head.
Since God is the one to take care of punishing others you don't have to go there. Instead, you can go on the offensive and try to encourage others. You may never change the consequences of God's vengeance in their eternity, but you will not be blamed for it because of your acts of kindness while on earth. Hunger and thirst are basic needs without which death is the ultimate consequence. Paul is not talking about making their life comfortable or sending them out to gorge on a smorgasbord, but treating with kindness those who will die if they don't eat or drink. Those who have attacked you and sought to destroy everything you stand for may be in huge need some day. When the cancer comes, the tragedy takes place, or the sudden death of a loved one shocks your enemy, your love and kindness would be the last expected, but the most impacting that enemy may experience. How would you treat a thirsty dog or horse? How do you treat your plants? Are dogs, horses, and azaleas more important than people? What could such acts of love and kindness do for those who have made your life miserable? ____________________

____

____

To **heap coals of fire on his head**, means to excite in him feelings of painful regret. Maybe if the offender knew God or lived for God, they would not have treated you in such a way. How could your forgiveness and kindness impact their lives for eternity?

____

____

Forgive, and just let God do His work.

Saturday: Romans 12

Overcome evil with good!

Be not overcome of evil, but overcome evil with good. Romans 12:21

Don't let evil conquer you, get the best of you, or defeat you. Conquer evil by doing good, get the best of evil by doing good, defeat evil by doing good. Do good!

Be is an action verb: be something, be anything, be, be being. If life (like driving) were controlled by stoplights, "**be**" would be the green light. In life, don't apathetically sit at a red light and do nothing or go nowhere. Apathy loathes being! Don't apprehensively hang out at a yellow light living in fear or virtual paralysis. Apprehension fears being! What if I fail? What if people laugh at me? What if I get my feelings hurt? Be careful but not fearful! Go for the green light and be actively pursuing life, keep moving, keep doing, and keep being. If you had to rate your spiritual life by a stoplight color: red (apathy), yellow (apprehension), or green (action), what color would you choose? ______________________________

____

Be not

Negative! No way! "Read my lips. Not gonna do it!" NOT! Learn to be negative in a positive way. If someone tempts you to sin, simply say, "No thank you." Learning when to say "no" in life can save your heart from tons of hurt. Write out Proverbs 1:10.

____

____

____

List ten things that most of us need to say "no" to almost every day.

____

____

____

____

____

Be not overcome

The Greek word for **overcome** is *nikáœ* which means victory. To be victorious, prevail, conquer, subdue, defeat, triumph over, overpower, overthrow...to win! Nike-ized Christians are overcomers who refuse to be **overcome**. In the Olympic wrestling world, overcomers do not allow themselves to get pinned down on the mat. They may get knocked down (or even knocked out) but will get back on the mat and keep on fighting. Overcomers never give up! What does is take to **overcome** you? What keeps you from being victorious (*nikáœ*) in your daily devotions? ______________________________

____

____

What keeps you from being victorious (*nikáœ*) in your thought life? ______________

____

What keeps you from being victorious (*nikáœ*) in your battle with anger or fear?

____

____

____

Be not overcome of evil

How do you know if you are **overcome of evil**? If your thought life is out of control and you consistently give in to lustful thoughts, you are being controlled by lust. If you can entertain yourself with sensual movies, TV, or Internet sites that are sexually explicit, and it not bother you, you have been conquered by lust. How does Peter encourage us to deal with lust in 1 Peter 2:11? ______

______

How do you know if you are **overcome of evil**? If you can scream at your parents or your kids, and not humbly ask them to forgive you, you are controlled by anger. If you won't talk to some friends because they make you so mad, you have been conquered by anger. What practical advice does James give those struggling with anger and wrath in James 1:19-20?

______

How do you know if you are **overcome of evil**? If you cannot say "no" to friends, no matter what they are asking, you are controlled by fear. If you want so badly to be accepted that you start talking, acting, and thinking like evil friends, you have been overcome of fear. How did Paul encourage Timothy to deal with fear in 1 Timothy 1:7? ______

______

Be not overcome of evil, but overcome evil with good.

Be victorious over evil; prevail over evil; conquer evil; subdue evil; defeat evil; triumph over evil; overpower evil; win over evil! How? God will give the grace (the power and the desire) and, for this instance, the weapon. Choose your weapons! A gun? A knife? A lead pipe (in the library with Professor Plum)? How about **good**!!! That which is **good** is profitable, useful, excellent, distinguished, upright, top quality, and beneficial.What is **good** for now is **good** forever! What is **good** in God's eyes should be **good** in my eyes! What "**good**" is there in fear, anger, or lust? ______

How are they profitable for eternity? ______

How are they useful for today? ______

How are they excellent for tomorrow? ______

According to Titus 2:7-8, how can you embarrass those who attack you? ______

______

According to 1 Peter 2:12, how can you stop all rumors by making them unbelievable even to unbelievers? ______

______

According to Proverbs 15:1, how can you stop an angry mom, dad, brother, or sister? ______

______

For whatsoever is born of God overcometh the world: and this is the victory that overcometh the world, even our faith. Who is he that overcometh the world, but he that believeth that Jesus is the Son of God? 1 John 5:4-5

Ye are of God, little children, and have overcome them: because greater is He that is in you, than he that is in the world. 1 John 4:4

Be not overcome of evil, but overcome evil with good. Romans 12:21

Sunday Review and Meditation

"Lord, thank You for saving me from my sin and delivering me from its consequences through Jesus Christ my Lord!"

Love others so much that you can rejoice and weep with them.

Read Monday's study and explain how the principles of Romans 12:15 have impacted your life.

Humbly enjoy the company of all of God's family.

Read Tuesday's study and explain how the truths of Romans 12:16 have challenged your life.

Respect others and refuse to retaliate for any reason.

Read Wednesday's study and explain how the teaching of Romans 12:17 has convicted you.

Live peaceably with all men (if it is possible).

Read Thursday's study and explain how the command of Romans 12:18 has altered your life.

Forgive. Don't retaliate. Let God do His just work.

Read Friday's study and explain how the confrontation of Romans 12:19-20 has made you think.

Overcome evil with good!

Read Saturday's study and explain how the exhortation of Romans 12:21 can change your life.

Therefore...

I beseech you therefore, brethren, by the mercies of God, that you present your bodies a living sacrifice, holy, acceptable unto God, which is your reasonable service.

Well, six weeks have flown by, and we are at the end of our study. It is good to be reminded of some thoughts from the beginning of our study.

How many things does a person have to know in order to live and die a happy, contented, fulfilled life? According to the Heidelberg Catechism he needs to know only three: one, how great are my miseries and sin; two, how I can be delivered from my misery and sin; and three, how I am to be thankful to God for such deliverance.

When Paul wrote the word "therefore" he was not just giving a general glimpse of the 315 verses of Romans 1-11, but he was specifically explaining man's complete ruin in sin (Romans 1-3) and God's perfect remedy in Christ (Romans 4-11). Knowing what we were and what God has done should impact the way we live each day.

Strong Bible teaching should always be accompanied by solid Bible application. Doctrine without application could give us big heads and little hearts. Application without doctrine could result in full hearts and empty heads.

It is not difficult to understand the extreme wickedness of our own hearts, but it is difficult to clearly explain what God has done for us and why He would treat such wicked sinners with such love. The conclusion of Romans 11 reveals to us how untraceable and unsearchable God's deliverance, mercy, and grace to us really is.

I trust you enjoyed your study of Romans 12 and the many ways you can say "Thank You!" to such a wonderful God who has done so much for you. Live your life thanking God for what He has done for you.

Overwhelmed with what God has done for me,

Rand

Rand Hummel

ENDNOTES

1. Warren Wiersbe, *Be Right: How to be Right with God, Yourself, and Others (An Expository Study of Romans),* (Colorado Springs: Chariot, 1978), New Edition.
2. Warren Wiersbe, *Expository Outlines of the New Testament,* (Wheaton: Victor, 1996).
3. Donald Grey Barnhouse, *Romans: Expositions of Bible Doctrines*, (Grand Rapids: Eerdmans, 1966).
4. Wiersbe.
5. William Hendriksen, *New Testament Commentary*, (Grand Rapids: Baker, 2002).
6. Joseph Hall, *A Selection from the Writings of Joseph Hall: With Observations of Some Specialities in His Life*, (Andover: Allen, Morrill & Wardwell, 1845).
7. Spiros Zodhiates, *The Complete Word Study Dictionary of the New Testament*, (Chattanooga: AMG, 1992).
8. Horst Balz, *The Exegetical Dictionary of the New Testament*, (Grand Rapids: Eerdmans, 1993).
9. John Stott, *The Message of Romans*, (Downers Grove: InterVarsity, 2001).
10. Zodhiates.
11. Joseph Henry Thayer, *New Testament Lexicon*, (New York: Harper & Brothers, 1889).
12. Hendricksen.
13. Barnhouse.
14. Ibid.
15. Ibid.
16. Zodhiates.
17. John F. MacArthur, Jr., *The MacArthur New Testament Commentary*, (Chicago: Moody, 1998).

Since 1969, THE WILDS Christian Camp and Conference Center has been serving the local church with a wide variety of camping programs. Our summer season, with over 11,000 campers, focuses on juniors with our Junior Boot Camp, teens with our junior high/senior high camps, and families with our week-long Family Camps. Fall and spring bring an entirely different look to the mountains and a different array of camps including Couples' Retreats, school and church retreats, high school Senior Trips, Senior High Leadership Camps, Ladies' Retreats, Father/Son Campouts, Senior Adult Retreats, College and Career Retreats, and specialized conferences including a Music Conference, a Youth Workers' Conference, Deacons' Conferences, and a Pastors' Conference. During this non-summer season we annually serve more than 10,000 campers of all ages.

THE WILDS is located in the beautiful Blue Ridge Mountains of western North Carolina and is a stunning piece of God's handiwork. Blessed with four spectacular waterfalls, meandering streams, and miles of hiking trails on the property, the campsite shows forth the handiwork of God. In this beautiful setting, thousands of campers of every age have accepted Christ as Saviour and Lord and have surrendered to His will and to His service.

Natural outgrowths of this active camp ministry are a music publication ministry, offering the most refreshing of conservative Christian music, cantatas, CDs, a song and chorus book, piano books, and choral books for men, ladies, and mixed groups.

As an outgrowth of the strong preaching and teaching ministries of the camp, THE WILDS has produced a great variety of Bible study helps, scripture memory programs, personal devotional helps, and books for individuals and group studies.

In addition, CampsAbroad, the missions arm of THE WILDS, assists missionaries and nationals all over the world in the development and operation of Christian camp ministries. In 2009 THE WILDS of New England began ministry operations at our campsite in Deering, New Hampshire. In this peaceful, rural setting we anticipate a steady growth and planned development toward a year-round camp and conference ministry for this area of the country.

For more information about any of our camping programs, music publications, or other products from THE WILDS, please visit our website at www. wilds. org, or contact the administrative office:

THE WILDS Christian Association, Inc.
PO Box 509
Taylors, SC 29687-0009
Phone: (864) 268-4760 • Fax: (864) 292-0743
E-mail: info@wilds.org